Statistical estimation of linear
economic relationships

Statistical estimation of linear economic relationships

Distributed lags and simultaneous equations

Y. P. GUPTA
Indian Agricultural Research Institute, New Delhi

With a foreword by A. L. Nagar
Professor of economics

Rotterdam University Press / 1971

ISBN 90 237 2228 0

Foreword

This book is an outcome of the research of Dr. Y. P. Gupta which he carried out at the Delhi School of Economics for his Ph.D. and later his post doctoral work at the Econometric Institute of The Netherlands School of Economics. He has provided a good treatment of the estimation techniques used in distributed lag models and has given a new method of estimation. Discussion on simultaneous equation methods is restricted to the two-stage least-squares procedure of Theil. He provides some new finite sample results in this connection.

A. L. Nagar

Acknowledgements

This publication is a revised version of my Ph.D. thesis which was submitted to the Delhi University in 1968. The research work which led to the thesis was carried out under the supervision of Professor A. L. Nagar to whom I am deeply indebted for valuable guidance, constant advice and keen interest. Comments and criticisms by the examiners and, in particular, by Professor Carl F. Christ were extremely helpful in finalizing the present work. At the Netherlands School of Economics, I am especially grateful to Professor W. H. Sommermeyer for valuable suggestions and continued encouragement. Thanks are also due to Dr. M. Hazewinkel for useful discussions on certain points. Finally, I wish to express my thanks to Mr. F. A. Palm for computing assistance, Mrs. L. H. A. Molleman for extending all possible library facilities, the Misses E. E. van Gelderen and J. G. E. G. Oosthout for typing and several others who in their own ways helped me in the preparation of the book.

Y. P. Gupta

Contents

CHAPTER 1. INTRODUCTION   11
1.1   Preliminaries   11
1.2   Problems in the Estimation of Distributed Lag Models   12
1.3   Estimating Techniques   13
1.4   Estimation of Simultaneous Economic Relationships   14
1.5   Plan of the Following Chapters   15

CHAPTER 2. DISTRIBUTED LAGS AND THEIR STATISTICAL ESTIMATION   17
2.1   Introduction   17
2.2   Distributed Lags and their Causes   17
2.3   Alternative Specifications of the Distributed Lag Model   20
2.4   Methods of Estimation   25

CHAPTER 3. PROPERTIES OF THE LIVIATAN'S ESTIMATOR   43
3.1   Introduction   43
3.2   Matrix Formulation of the Model (2.3.5)   43
3.3   Statement of Theorems   47
3.4   Proof of Theorem I   51
3.5   Proof of Theorem II   54
3.6   Proof of Theorem III   54
3.7   Proof of Theorem IV   57

CHAPTER 4. AN ITERATIVE INSTRUMENTAL VARIABLES ESTIMATOR OF (2.3.5)   62
4.1   Introduction   62
4.2   The Estimator   62
4.3   Estimation of the model – an Empirical Analysis   66
4.4   Conclusions   69

9

CHAPTER 5. ESTIMATION OF SIMULTANEOUS LINEAR
EQUATIONS   74
   5.1 Introduction   74
   5.2 The Structural Equation System   74
   5.3 Identifiability Criteria in Linear Models   75
   5.4 Matrix Formulation of the Model   77
   5.5 Assumptions   79
   5.6 The Two-Stage Least Squares   80

CHAPTER 6. PROPERTIES OF THE TWO-STAGE LEAST SQUARES
ESTIMATORS   82
   6.1 Introduction   82
   6.2 Theorems on the Moment Matrix of the Two-Stage Least
      Squares Estimators and Bias of the Covariance Matrix of
      Disturbances   83
   6.3 Proof of Theorem I   88
   6.4 Proof of Theorem II   93

   Appendix to Chapter 6
   (A) Moments of an M-Dimensional Normal Distribution   96
   (B) Expectations Required for Proving Theorem I Stated in
      Section 6.2   96

CHAPTER 7. A NUMERICAL EXAMPLE: APPLICATION TO
KLEIN'S MODEL I   105
   7.1 Introduction   105
   7.2 Description of the Model   105
   7.3 Computational Procedure and the Results   106

REFERENCES   112

INDEX   115

1. Introduction

1.1 PRELIMINARIES

In economics as well as in social sciences, one is usually faced with the problem of describing a certain phenomenon which may be the net result of an interplay of multiplicity of forces. For example, if we are considering the problem of explaining the demand for sugar in a certain market, one may imagine this to be affected by its price and the prices of its substitutes besides other factors. Similarly, the economy of a country may be considered as an interplay of large number of economic and non-economic variables. Several times it is possible to lay down proper functional relationships between relevant economic variables for this purpose. Tinbergen (1937, 1939, 1951) introduced the concept of explaining the structure of an economy with the help of a set of such relationships.[1] Recent experiments in this direction have been made by Klein (1950), Klein-Goldberger (1955), Duesenberry, Fromm, Klein and Kuh (1965), etc. Single equation models are also very commonly used in most situations. As illustrations, we may mention the Cobb-Douglas production function and the CES production function proposed by Arrow, Chenery, Minhas and Solow (1961). These production functions relate the total output to inputs (capital and labour).

Several times one finds that the functional relationships involved are non-linear. The Brookings Econometric Model for the U.S. economy is highly non-linear in both parameters and variables. Similarly, the CES production function is non-linear in parameters. In such cases sometimes it is possible to overcome the difficulty by devising suitable methods in particular cases or by making use of linear approximations. In some cases suitable transformation of variables may lead to linear relationships. For example, in case of the Cobb-Douglas production function the relationship between the logarithms of original variables is linear. A large number of such examples are available in the literature.

The variables entering the functional relationships may relate to the same period of time or to different periods. In economic dynamics it is

11

a common practice to use current and lagged variables in the formulation of economic relations. Such economic relations may be motivated due to several reasons. For example, it may be argued that the current year total consumption is the net effect of incomes of current and all past years. One might also argue differently by saying that a change in the price of a certain commodity disturbs the market equilibrium instantaneously and it takes some time before the equilibrium is restored.

In the present work we shall be dealing with problems involved in the estimation of distributed lag models and also we shall consider some problems relating to the estimation of general equation system.

1.2 PROBLEMS IN THE ESTIMATION OF DISTRIBUTED LAG MODELS

In the statistical estimation of a linear distributed lag model of the type

$$q_t = \alpha p_t + \alpha_1 p_{t-1} + \alpha_2 p_{t-2} + \ldots + u_t, \tag{1.2.1}$$

where

q_t = quantity demanded of a certain commodity at time t
p_t = price of the commodity at time t,

one faces two basic difficulties:
a. the number of parameters to be estimated is infinite
b. the explanatory variables will normally be highly inter-correlated, leading to large standard errors of coefficient estimates.

If, however, we follow Koyck's specification of geometric lag structure

$$\alpha_i = \alpha \beta^i, \quad i = 1, 2, \ldots$$

with $0 \leqslant \beta < 1$, then, in effect, we are assuming that the influences of prices in past go on diminishing in geometric progression as we go farther away from the current period. This is not an unrealistic assumption. Moreover, in that case the model in (1.2.1) can be transformed to an elegant form:

$$q_t = \alpha p_t + \beta q_{t-1} + w_t, \quad w_t = u_t - \beta u_{t-1}. \tag{1.2.2}$$

This formulation is much simpler to handle because now there are only two explanatory variables involved in the model. Moreover, the correlation between the variables[2] p_t and q_{t-1} is usually much less than that between the variables p_t, p_{t-1}, p_{t-2}, etc. For statistical estimation of the coefficients of the model (1.2.2) based on the time series observations, we need an estimation method which takes into account the implications of

12

stochastic dependence among the successive $\{u_t\}$[3]. These disturbances represent the aggregate effect of those (latent) variables of which no explicit account is taken in the model. Such a dependence among the disturbances is likely to have a reduced effect on the parameter estimates if both current and lagged variables are present in the model. According to Klein (1958) the use of q_{t-1} as an explanatory variable in (1.2.2) will extract most of the serial correlation among the errors, $\{u_t\}$. Thus, one may start out with the assumption that $\{u_t\}$ are uncorrelated having the same probability distribution. However, in this particular case this simplifying assumption is not of much value because the composite disturbances, $\{w_t\}$, in (1.2.2) remain autocorrelated irrespective of the fact whether the disturbances, $\{u_t\}$, in the original model are autocorrelated or not. The same is true with the correlation between the variables q_{t-1} and w_t. It follows that as such an application of classical least squares theory to (1.2.2) would not produce parameter estimates possessing desirable properties [for a discussion of these properties, see Koopmans and Hood (1953, p. 128)].

In the present analysis we shall consider the problem of estimation of the model (1.2.2) under the general assumption that $\{u_t\}$ are autocorrelated and follow a first order Markov process with ϱ as the parameter (unknown) of autoregression.[4]

1.3 ESTIMATING TECHNIQUES

The alternative methods of estimation which we shall examine in the following chapters are listed below:
a. Least squares
b. Koyck's scanning method
c. Klein's iterative procedure
d. Liviatan's instrumental variables approach
e. Hannan's method based on spectral analysis
f. Amemiya and Fuller's iterative method
g. Dhrymes' search procedure.

We shall also propose a method in this connection.

It is well known that the first of these methods, though straightforward, yields inconsistent estimates of the parameters of the model (1.2.2).[5] This difficulty arises due to the fact that one of the basic assumptions underlying the least squares theory, viz. zero correlation between q_{t-1} and w_t in the population, is violated. Koyck's method of estimation of distributed lags is consistent but the procedure applies only to those cases where the magnitude of the autocorrelation coefficient, ϱ, is known *a priori*. Klein's iterative method of estimating (1.2.2) uses least squares estimate of ϱ in the first round of iteration. Since such an estimate of ϱ is inconsistent, the consistency of the final estimates, to which the process would converge, is not ensured.[6] Liviatan's consistent method using instrumental variables is free of, at least, these troubles and is simple from computations viewpoint. As a matter of fact, there is a one to one correspondence between the least squares method and the instrumental variables approach [for details, see Goldberger (1964, p. 285)]. Since, there are, in general, more instruments available than the number actually required in any practical situation, the real problem involved in the application of the latter method, therefore, lies in their selection. Further, we have Hannan's estimation procedure which is consistent and asymptotically efficient. But its use, in practice, is restricted to situations admitting large sample size. Another method which is also asymptotically equivalent to the maximum likelihood procedure is due to Amemiya and Fuller. The authors claim that the estimates can be obtained with a modest amount of computational work. Finally, we have a method due to Dhrymes which requires, in addition to other assumptions, a specification of the normal distribution of the disturbances, $\{u_t\}$. The parameter estimates which globally maximize the likelihood function for every sample size are consistent, asymptotically unbiased and efficient. These are indeed attractive features of the estimating technique. Unfortunately, the computational procedure is not straightforward and involves a great deal of work, a point which does not support the use of the method in several situations.

In Koyck's method, instead of scanning the range of the autocorrelation coefficient one may think of estimating ϱ originally from Liviatan's formula and then make its use in the computations of Koyck's estimates. Similarly, in Klein's method the difficulty posed by Malinvaud may be overcome by using a consistent estimate of ϱ in the initial stage of the iterative procedure.

1.4 ESTIMATION OF SIMULTANEOUS ECONOMIC RELATIONSHIPS

In the more general case of simultaneous equations we actually have a vector of dependent (endogenous) variables 'to be explained' in terms of predetermined variables which may consist of lagged endogenous and/or current and lagged exogenous variables. These variables are connected by several functional relationships forming an interdependent system of equations. Lots of theories have been discussed in the literature on several aspects of simultaneous equation systems.

14

The method of estimation to be analyzed in the present work is Theil's two-stage least squares. Its asymptotic properties have been discussed by Theil.

The covariance matrices of coefficient estimates for individual equations provide the standard errors. The covariances of estimates of coefficients are sometimes required to test the significance of a linear combination of two coefficients. We shall analyze these covariances, to order $1/T^2$ (T being the sample size) in probability, of coefficient estimates in two different equations of the complete system of simultaneous equations.

Another problem to be dealt with relates to the estimation of the covariance matrix of the structural disturbances according to the two-stage least squares method. The diagonal elements of the matrix provide estimates of variances in individual equations and the off-diagonal elements give estimates of covariances between different equations. We shall analyze the bias, to order $1/T$, of these covariance estimates.

1.5 PLAN OF THE FOLLOWING CHAPTERS[7]

The following is the arrangement of contents of the book. There are seven chapters in all. Chapters 2, 3 and 4 deal with the problems of estimation of distributed lags while the last three chapters have been devoted to the problems of estimation of simultaneous equations.

Chapter 2 introduces the concept of distributed lags and deals with the basic problem of their estimation. A brief survey of alternative methods of estimation of the distributed lag model assuming geometric lag structure is given in the last section of the chapter. Chapter 3 is devoted entirely to the small sample properties of the consistent estimator proposed by Liviatan. The results on the bias, to order $1/T$, the moment matrix, to order $1/T^2$, of the consistent estimator are derived in the chapter. The bias, to order $1/T$, of the residual variance estimator (according to Liviatan's procedure) is also analyzed in this chapter. In Chapter 4 an alternative method of estimating the same model is developed. An illustration has been presented in the last section of the chapter giving numerical magnitudes of the parameter estimates of the distributed lag model obtained by applying different estimating techniques to it.

Chapter 5 briefly describes the general equation system and the two-stage least squares method along with the underlying assumptions. Chapter 6 is concerned with the derivation of the moment matrix (to order $1/T^2$) of the two-stage least squares estimates of coefficients in different equations (i-th and j-th) of the complete system of simultaneous equations. The bias,

15

to order $1/T$, of the covariance matrix of the structural disturbances according to this method is also given. The last chapter of the book is used to illustrate these results numerically.

NOTES

1. He classified these relations into four categories as: (a) behaviour (b) technical (c) institutional and (d) definitional.
2. For convenience no distinction will be made between the name of a variable and an observation on it. This should cause no confusion.
3. $\{u_t\}$ denotes the sequence of observations $u_1, \ldots, u_t$ on the random variable u.
4. This specification is sufficiently realistic if the period of observation is annual or quarter. But in case of monthly or weekly data it may not be true [cf. Malinvaud (1966), footnote marked '+', p. 438].
5. For a brief discussion of the properties of consistency and unbiasedness, cf. Chapter 2, Section 4.
6. Cf. Malinvaud (1961).
7. Some of the results presented in Chapters 3 and 6 have been published. For references, see Gupta (1968), Nagar and Gupta (1968, 1970) and Misra and Gupta (1971).

2. Distributed lags and their statistical estimation

2.1 INTRODUCTION

Irving Fisher (1937) was the first to introduce and discuss the concept of distributed lags in the context of econometric applications. He presented a statistical exposition of the problem of estimating reaction coefficients by making an appropriate assumption about the form of their distribution. Subsequently, Alt (1942) and Tinbergen (1949) also attempted to solve the estimation problem before Koyck (1954) could successfully carry out a systematic study and present its implications. He exploited the field of distributed lags while studying investment behaviour and related problems and since then it has become a convenient and workable econometric tool in economic analysis. He removed some of the bottlenecks in the statistical treatment of the distributed lags but could not eliminate them all completely. Still his approach was quite promising and realistic in practice and left a wide scope for further research. After his pioneering work several alternative estimation techniques have been proposed with an aim to present the solution of the estimation problem in a simple and general form.

This chapter is devoted to the study of alternative methods of estimation proposed by various authors. In surveying different estimators we shall, however, restrict ourselves to the study of a distributed lag model with geometrically declining series of coefficients as proposed by Koyck.

2.2 DISTRIBUTED LAGS AND THEIR CAUSES[1]

Day to day observations in a competitive market reveal that a change in the price of a commodity affects its quantity demanded. In general, a fall in price leads to an increase in demand and vice-versa. If we observe this demand-price relationship over time we shall often note that the response of demand to a change in price of a commodity which persists over a sufficiently long period is gradually adaptive rather than instantaneous. For example, consider the response of a large number of consumers to a sudden fall in the price of one commodity, say tea. Obviously, all the consumers will not react to it at once and at the same point of time. Some will react immediately or after a short time and some slowly for various reasons. They may delay their response for lack of precise knowledge of the market and may take some time to learn and then to find alternative choices before they are able to act at last. The remaining ones may not respond at all for known or unknown reasons. Consequently, the total reaction of all the consumers will be spread over some length of time. Sometimes this effect will be confined to a short interval but in many cases the adjustment process will be distributed over a long period of time. While studying the behaviour of producers and suppliers with respect to changes in price we come across a similar situation. This type of behaviour of consumers or producers gives rise to a 'distributed lag'.

Thus an 'economic reaction' or simply a reaction caused by a change in the price of a certain commodity on its quantity demanded or supplied is a process over time. It may continue either for a short or for a long time. In such cases it may be important for economic analysis to work out these reactions during different periods of time till the adjustment process is complete. Moreover, the cumulative effect of a reaction may increase with a large lag and converge to some equilibrium value in the long run.

Suppose the equilibrium value of the quantity demanded of a certain commodity is q_t in the period t. Then this can be considered as the net effect of changes in current price and prices in the past. As a linear approximation we may express this analytically as[2]

$$q_t = \alpha_0 p_t + \alpha_1 p_{t-1} + \ldots$$

where the sequence $p_t, p_{t-1}, \ldots$ of prices during periods $t, t-1, \ldots$, may be finite or infinite. The constants $\alpha_0, \alpha_1, \ldots$ are the reaction coefficients.[3] Similarly when analyzing the consumption or investment function one may relate the current year's consumption or investment with incomes of the current and preceding years.

Suppose that an equilibrium situation is disturbed due to a finite change in the price and that it persists indefinitely. If it results in a new equilibrium then obviously the corresponding change in the quantity demanded will be finite. This implies that the total reaction measured by $\sum_{i=0}^{\infty} \alpha_i$ must be finite. This leads to the following restriction on the elements of the sequence $\{\alpha_i\}$:

$$\lim_{t \to \infty} \alpha_i = 0$$

18

In general, let us write a linear distributed lag model with discrete lags as

$$y_t = \alpha_0 x_t + \alpha_1 x_{t-1} + \ldots + u_t, \tag{2.2.1}$$

where y_t is the value of the left hand dependent variable 'to be explained' in period t, and x_t, x_{t-1}, ... is the sequence of observations on the explanatory variable in periods t, $t - 1$, ..., respectively. u_t is the value of the disturbance in period t. The sequence α_0, α_1, ... of coefficients is bounded and describes the 'form of the lag distribution' or the 'time shape of the economic reaction'.[4]

In case (2.2.1) is a consumption function such that y_t is the aggregate consumption in period t and x_t is the aggregate income in the same period, α_0 may be interpreted as the 'short-run marginal propensity to consume' and $\sum_{i=0}^{\infty} \alpha_i$ as the 'long-run marginal propensity to consume'. Thus, the effect of a sudden change in the value of x in the current period t is measured by α_0 and the effect of a gradual and *pari passu* change in x over the entire past is measured through $\sum_{i=0}^{\infty} \alpha_i$.

The 'speed of adjustment', that is, the speed with which the adjustment process is completed, also plays an important rôle in determining the stability of equilibrium in dynamic situations. For example, the reaction of a manufacturing firm to a sudden increase in demand of a particular commodity will be much faster than the reaction to an immediate fall in demand of the same commodity.

The usefulness of distributed lags is much discussed in the econometric literature.[5] These are valuable particularly when the adjustment process is progressive along the time axis. A growing applicability of distributed lag models in econometric investigations is an indication of their great relevance. Models involving lagged dependent variables have proved useful in the long-run analyses of consumer behaviour, investment behaviour, inventory, etc. The knowledge of short-run effects may be valuable in studies relating to employment, price inflation, etc., while that of long-run effects is of great significance in prediction and forecasting for long term policy matters.

There are several reasons for the existence of distributed lags. These are grouped into three broad categories.
1. *Technological reasons* – arise in the production of durable, investment and consumer goods;
2. *Institutional reasons* – are due to government regulations and customs;
3. *Psychological reasons* – refer to factors such as habit persistence, inertia and imperfect knowledge of the market.

To illustrate these we may quote Professor T. M. Brown's (1952, p. 359) remark made when testing for the existence of lags in the consumption function. According to him 'the lag effect in consumer demand was produced by the consumption *habits* which people formed as a result of past consumption. The habits, customs, standards, and levels associated with real consumption previously enjoyed become "impressed" on the human physiological and psychological systems and this produces an inertia or "hysteresis" in consumer behaviour. Because of this inertia, consumer demand reacts to changes in consumer income with a certain slowness, and thus past real consumption exerts a stabilizing effect on current consumption'. Response of employment to productivity changes, the entire process of industrial or agricultural production, shipment of goods from one place to another, regular payment of instalments of loans or insurance premiums, each at the end of some fixed period of time are all examples of lagged effects.

2.3 ALTERNATIVE SPECIFICATIONS OF THE DISTRIBUTED LAG MODEL

At this stage two basic difficulties of a statistical nature with regard to the model (2.2.1) are worth mentioning. First, in any practical situation there is generally a lack of information about the relevant economic variables. For example, in economic time series analysis we often have too small a number of observations to justify the application of ordinary least squares method directly to (2.2.1). The second difficulty as Alt (1942) has demonstrated arises due to the presence of too many lagged independent variables in the model. In practice these variables are likely to exhibit a high degree of multicollinearity which might give a distorted picture of the time shape of an economic reaction. To get around these problems some particularization of the model is thus necessary.

In this connection Fisher (1937) suggested that we may approximate the shape of the lag distribution by means of a 'logarithmically normal' probability curve as shown in figure 2.1a. This distribution implies that the effect of a given variable x_t on y_t is very small at first, rises fast to its mode value and then decreases gradually. Since the method involves a considerable amount of computational effort, later he made a simplifying assumption about the form of lag distribution. According to his second assumption the effect of any given variable may be assumed 'to be the greatest at the very next time unit and then to taper off by equal decrements for each successive time unit. That is, the distribution curve becomes a straight line, beginning one time unit after the cause'. The shape of this distribution is given in Figure 2.1b.[6]

Figure 2.1   Alternative approximations of the time shape of a reaction

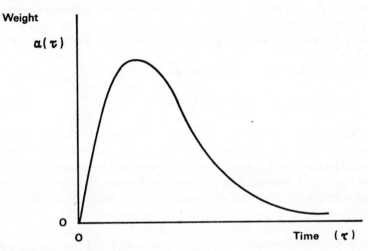

Figure 2.1a. *Log-normal curve*

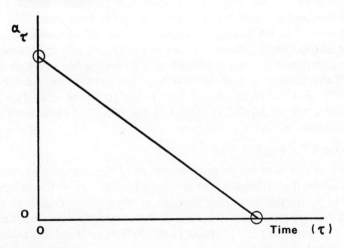

Figure 2.1b. *Linear curve*

Another plausible distribution of lag is a geometric curve proposed by Koyck. He suggested that the following restrictions be imposed on the reaction coefficients of the model (2.2.1):

$$\alpha_{k+i} = \alpha\beta^i, \quad i = 0, 1, \ldots \tag{2.3.1}$$

where $0 \leq \beta < 1$ and the index k represents the point from which onwards the parametric approximation starts. It may be zero or some other prefixed positive integer. The coefficient β is a lag parameter and declines geometrically over time.[7]

Substituting (2.3.1) into (2.2.1) we get

$$y_t = \sum_{i=0}^{k-1} \alpha_i x_{t-i} + \alpha(x_{t-k} + \beta x_{t-k-1} + \beta^2 x_{t-k-2} + \ldots) + u_t. \tag{2.3.2}$$

In effect, the hypothesis (2.3.1) implies that beyond a certain point in time, say $i = k$, successive prices in the past have an exponentially diminishing effect on demand. This assumption has been recognized to be fairly realistic in practice. For instance, the framework adopted in formulating Cagan's (1956) 'adaptive expectations' or Nerlove's (1958) 'partial adjustment' model leads essentially to the assumption of an exponentially decaying lag structure. What is perhaps more interesting is their satisfactory performance in economic applications. To give some examples, Palda's (1964) study employs Koyck's distributed lag model and measures adequately the long-run effects of advertising on sales, Nerlove's partial adjustment model has been used successfully in studying the demand for durable goods – see Harberger (1960); the rationale behind Cagan's adaptive expectations model has been employed by Friedman (1957, p. 143) in the context of his 'permanent income hypothesis' of consumption, etc.

The above considerations sufficiently justify our choice of studying a linear distributed lag model subject to a geometric lag structure. In the rest of this chapter and in the next two chapters we shall be concerned primarily with the problems involved in the statistical estimation of the distributed lag model (2.2.1) subject to the following restrictions on the coefficients $\alpha_0, \alpha_1, \ldots$

$$\alpha_i = \alpha\beta^i, \quad i = 0, 1, \ldots \tag{2.3.3}$$

where $0 \leq \beta < 1$ is the stability condition of the economic system.[8] The specification $\beta < 1$ implies that the lagged influences of the independent variable x_t on the dependent variable y_t taper off according as the lag increases. The reason for assuming $\beta \geq 0$ is that it seems unlikely that the coefficients in (2.2.1) alternate in sign.[9] The coefficient α is assumed to be bounded.

Consequently, (2.2.1) simplifies to[10]

$$y_t = \alpha x_t + \alpha\beta x_{t-1} + \alpha\beta^2 x_{t-2} + \ldots + u_t, \tag{2.3.4}$$

or

$$y_t = \alpha x_t + \beta(\alpha x_{t-1} + \alpha\beta x_{t-2} + \ldots + u_{t-1}) + (u_t - \beta u_{t-1})$$

and, finally, in terms of two explanatory variables

$$y_t = \alpha x_t + \beta y_{t-1} + w_t, \quad w_t = u_t - \beta u_{t-1}. \tag{2.3.5}$$

Thus the attractive feature of Koyck's assumption of approximating the whole adjustment path of y_t by a geometric series lies in the fact that both the difficulties associated with the general model are overcome to a great extent.[11]

Unless otherwise stated our analysis of the model (2.3.4) will be based on the following assumptions:

Assumption 1. T real-valued time series observations are available on the dependent variable y_t and the independent variable x_t which are measured without error.

This assumption specifies the amount of sample information available on the economic variables y_t and x_t, say representing consumption and disposable income respectively, which are assumed to be related in a way described by the behaviour equation (2.3.4). Furthermore, it restricts the analysis to situations in which the variables are observed without errors of measurement.

Assumption 2. The variable x_t is non-stochastic and fixed in repeated samples and, hence, it is statistically independent of the variable u_t and in turn of the composite disturbance w_t for all t.

Assumption 3. The disturbance u_t is an unobservable random variable such that[12]

$$Eu_t = 0, \quad Eu_t^2 = \sigma_u^2 \,(\textit{finite})$$

and is distributed independently of both x_t and t $(t = 1, 2, \ldots, T)$.

This means that the mean and variance of the probability distribution of the variable u_t exist and are finite. An assumption about its expected value is required in order that the parameters α and β in (2.3.4) are identifiable. Otherwise, the two structures identified by, say (a) $\alpha = 0$, $Eu = x$ and (b) $\alpha = 1$, $\beta = 0$, $Eu = 0$ would result in the same conditional distribution of the variable y_t – see Malinvaud (1966, p. 75). The assumed property of equal variances over time implies that the distribution of u_t remains unchanged from one period to another. This assumption is generally satisfied in time series investigations conducted at macro-level.

Assumption 4. u_t follows a first-order Markov scheme

$$u_t = \varrho u_{t-1} + e_t, \qquad 0 \leqslant |\varrho| < 1$$

with ϱ as the parameter of autoregression and e_t a random variable such that

$$Ee_t = 0, \text{ and } E(e_t e_{t'}) = \delta_{tt'} \sigma^2,$$

the value of $\delta_{tt'}$ being unity whenever $t = t'$ and zero otherwise.

This means that u_t is correlated with its previous values while e_t is not. An assumption of this type is of vital importance in economic time series analysis. In many econometric studies it is believed that the factors which give rise to disturbances in behavioural equations behave systematically from one time period to another; such a behaviour of the errors can be adequately described by the first order autoregressive process as presented above. One of the main findings of Cochrane and Orcutt (1949) is that '... the error terms involved in most current formulations of economic relations are highly positively correlated' and 'the presence of autocorrelated error terms requires some modification of the usual least squares method of estimation'. A remark by Malinvaud (1966, p. 420) is also worth citing. It says that 'too strong a time dependence among the errors often indicates some flaw in the model. Some important factors have probably not been recognized. It is better to investigate them and introduce them explicitly than to keep an incomplete model which may lead to wrong interpretations'. Thus the existence of correlation between the errors may add to the problems involved in both specification and estimation aspects of econometric analysis. However, for our study of the latter aspect we shall always treat the above model and underlying assumptions 'true' and 'valid' in any particular situation.

Of these, the first two assumptions deal with the observable variables y_t and x_t and the last two characterize the probability distribution of the unobservable random disturbance u_t.

The above formulation immediately leads to the following results:

$$u_t = e_t + \varrho e_{t-1} + \varrho^2 e_{t-2} + \ldots, \tag{2.3.6}$$

and, therefore, for an infinite series

$$\sigma_u^2 = \sigma^2/(1 - \varrho^2), \tag{2.3.7}$$

which is independent of t as required by Assumption 3. Furthermore, for two different periods t and t' $(= 1, \ldots, T)$

$$E(u_t u_{t'}) = E\{(e_t + \varrho e_{t-1} + \varrho^2 e_{t-2} + \ldots)(e_{t'} + \varrho e_{t'-1} + \ldots)\}$$
$$= \varrho^{|t-t'|} \sigma_u^2, \qquad (2.3.8)$$

and, in particular,

$$E(u_t u_{t'}) = \varrho \sigma_u^2 = \varrho \sigma^2/(1 - \varrho^2), \qquad \text{for } t' = t - 1$$
$$= \sigma_u^2, \qquad \text{for } t' = t. \qquad (2.3.9)$$

Moreover, by virtue of (2.3.7) and (2.3.9) the first-order autocorrelation coefficient between u_t's is given by

$$\frac{\text{cov}\,(u_t, u_{t-1})}{\text{var}\,u_{t(-1)}} = \frac{E(u_t u_{t-1})}{E u_{t(-1)}^2} = \varrho. \qquad (2.3.10)$$

Sometimes, we shall require a knowledge of the exact form of the probability distribution and temporal independence of the variable u_t as given below.

Assumption 5. The random variable u_t is independently and identically distributed and follows a normal distribution with zero mean and constant variance σ_u^2.

2.4 METHODS OF ESTIMATION[13]

Having stated the model and underlying assumptions the problem of statistical estimation of the parameters α and β will now be dealt with. The estimating techniques to be discussed below are those proposed by Koyck (1954), Klein (1958), Liviatan (1963), Hannan (1965), Amemiya and Fuller (1967), and Dhrymes (1969). It would appear that some of these estimators are of historical interest only, as they fail to take into account explicitly the autocorrelation properties of the disturbances. This is because of *a priori* specification of the unknown nature of autocorrelation between the disturbances. The last three methods are consistent and asymptotically efficient.

Least Squares Method

The simplest of methods of estimation of the lag model (2.3.5) is the method of ordinary least squares (OLS). According to this method the sum of squares of errors given by[14]

$$\Sigma w_t^2 = \Sigma (y_t - \alpha x_t - \beta y_{t-1})^2 \qquad (2.4.1)$$

25

is minimized with respect to the parameters α and β. Denoting OLS estimators of α and β by a and b, respectively, the normal equations to be solved are given in the matrix form as

$$\begin{bmatrix} \Sigma x_t^2 & \Sigma x_t y_{t-1} \\ \Sigma x_t y_{t-1} & \Sigma y_{t-1}^2 \end{bmatrix} \begin{bmatrix} a \\ b \end{bmatrix} = \begin{bmatrix} \Sigma x_t y_t \\ \Sigma y_t y_{t-1} \end{bmatrix}. \tag{2.4.2}$$

Upon solving for a and b we get

$$a = \frac{1}{\Delta}(\Sigma y_{t-1}^2 \, \Sigma x_t y_t - \Sigma x_t y_{t-1} \, \Sigma y_t y_{t-1}) \tag{2.4.3}$$

and

$$b = \frac{1}{\Delta}(\Sigma x_t^2 \, \Sigma y_t y_{t-1} - \Sigma x_t y_{t-1} \, \Sigma x_t y_t) \tag{2.4.4}$$

with

$$\Delta = \Sigma x_t^2 \, \Sigma y_{t-1}^2 - (\Sigma x_t y_{t-1})^2, \tag{2.4.5}$$

assuming $\Delta \neq 0$.

In order to examine the properties of the OLS estimators a and b, we note that under the Assumptions 1 through 4 and if both β and ϱ are not equal to zero

$$E(w_t w_{t-1}) = E\{(u_t - \beta u_{t-1})(u_{t-1} - \beta u_{t-2})\}$$
$$= \sigma_u^2 (\varrho - \beta\varrho^2 - \beta + \beta^2\varrho) \neq 0, \tag{2.4.6}$$

implying autocorrelation between composite disturbances $\{w_t\}$ and

$$E(w_t y_{t-1}) = E\{(u_t - \beta u_{t-1})(\alpha x_{t-1} + \alpha\beta x_{t-2} + \ldots + u_{t-1})\}$$
$$= E\{(u_t - \beta u_{t-1})u_{t-1}\}$$
$$= (\varrho - \beta)\sigma_u^2 \neq 0, \tag{2.4.7}$$

showing again correlation between the explanatory variable y_{t-1} and the disturbance w_t. Clearly, a and b are biased.[15] Moreover, applying Slutsky's theorem [cf. Cramér (1946), p. 255] to the OLS vector of coefficient estimates we get[16]

$$\plim_{T \to \infty} \begin{pmatrix} a \\ b \end{pmatrix} - \begin{pmatrix} \alpha \\ \beta \end{pmatrix} = \plim_{T \to \infty} (Z'Z/T)^{-1} \plim_{T \to \infty} \begin{pmatrix} \Sigma x_t w_t/T \\ \Sigma y_{t-1} w_t/T \end{pmatrix}, \tag{2.4.8}$$

where

$$Z = \begin{bmatrix} x_2 & y_1 \\ \vdots & \vdots \\ x_T & y_{T-1} \end{bmatrix} \tag{2.4.9}$$

is a $(T-1) \times 2$ matrix of observations on the explanatory variables. Since

$$\text{plim}_{T\to\infty} \Sigma x_t w_t/T = 0 \text{ and plim}_{T\to\infty} \Sigma y_{t-1} w_t/T = (\varrho - \beta)\sigma_u^2 \neq 0, \qquad (2.4.10)$$

in view of the result (2.4.7) and if $\text{plim}_{T\to\infty} (Z'Z/T)^{-1}$ exists and is finite, we conclude that the OLS estimators a and b of α and β given by (2.4.2) are 'biased' and 'inconsistent'.[17]

Koyck's Estimation Procedure

As traditional least squares theory results in undesirable parameter estimates, Koyck has proposed the following two-step procedure for estimating (2.3.5).

Since

$$\text{plim}_{T\to\infty} \binom{a}{b} \text{ differs from } \binom{\alpha}{\beta}$$

by an amount

$$\text{plim}_{T\to\infty} (Z'Z/T)^{-1} \begin{bmatrix} 0 \\ (\varrho - \beta)\sigma_u^2 \end{bmatrix}, \qquad (2.4.11)$$

it suggests that the consistency of the estimators a and b can be recovered by subtracting from the vector of OLS estimators a factor whose 'plim' is equal to the expression given in (2.4.11). This will be achieved by proceeding as follows.

Consider the OLS estimated errors given by

$$\dot{w}_t = y_t - ax_t - by_{t-1}$$
$$= w_t - (a - \alpha)x_t - (b - \beta)y_{t-1}, \qquad (2.4.12)$$

and

$$\frac{\Sigma \dot{w}_t^2}{T} = \frac{\Sigma w_t^2}{T} - [(a - \alpha)\ (b - \beta)] \begin{bmatrix} \Sigma x_t w_t/T \\ \Sigma y_{t-1} w_t/T \end{bmatrix} \qquad (2.4.13)$$

yielding

$$\text{plim}_{T\to\infty} \frac{\Sigma \dot{w}_t^2}{T} = \{(1 - \beta\varrho) - (\varrho - \beta)\ \text{plim}_{T\to\infty} b\}\ \sigma_u^2, \qquad (2.4.14)$$

where use has been made of the result

$$Ew_t^2 = (1 + \beta^2 - 2\beta\varrho)\ \sigma_u^2, \qquad \text{for all } t.$$

27

Further, notice that

$$\operatorname*{plim}_{T\to\infty} \frac{(\varrho-\beta)\,\Sigma\dot{w}_t^2/T}{(1-\beta\varrho)-(\varrho-\beta)b} = (\varrho-\beta)\operatorname*{plim}_{T\to\infty}(\Sigma\dot{w}_t^2/T)\,/\{(1-\beta\varrho)-$$
$$-\,(\varrho-\beta)\operatorname*{plim}_{T\to\infty} b\} = (\varrho-\beta)\sigma_u^2, \qquad (2.4.15)$$

where the result given in (2.4.14) has been used. Obviously, the vector to be subtracted from the right hand vector in (2.4.2) is

$$\begin{bmatrix} 0 \\ \dfrac{(\varrho-\beta)\,\Sigma\dot{w}_t^2}{(1-\beta\varrho)-(\varrho-\beta)b} \end{bmatrix}. \qquad (2.4.16)$$

Hence, consistent estimates $\tilde{\alpha}$ and $\tilde{\beta}$ of α and β, respectively, are obtained by solving the following set of normal equations

$$\begin{bmatrix} \Sigma x_t^2 & \Sigma x_t y_{t-1} \\ \Sigma x_t y_{t-1} & \Sigma y_{t-1}^2 \end{bmatrix} \begin{bmatrix} \tilde{\alpha} \\ \tilde{\beta} \end{bmatrix} = \begin{bmatrix} \Sigma x_t y_t \\ \Sigma y_t y_{t-1} - \dfrac{(\varrho-\tilde{\beta})\,\Sigma\dot{w}_t^2}{(1-\tilde{\beta}\varrho)-(\varrho-\tilde{\beta})b} \end{bmatrix}, \quad (2.4.17)$$

where $\dot{w}_t$ is defined in (2.4.12). To solve this system we may proceed as follows:

From the first equation implied by (2.4.17) we obtain $\tilde{\alpha}$ in terms of $\tilde{\beta}$ as

$$\tilde{\alpha} = (\Sigma x_t y_t - \tilde{\beta}\Sigma x_t y_{t-1})\,/\,\Sigma x_t^2, \qquad (2.4.18)$$

and then substitute this into the second equation of (2.4.17). The resulting quadratic equation in $\tilde{\beta}$ will have two roots.[18] Corresponding to each of these we can derive a value of $\tilde{\alpha}$. Finally, we choose the pair $(\tilde{\alpha}, \tilde{\beta})$ which gives a smaller sum of squares of residuals in (2.3.5) and satisfies $0 \leqslant \tilde{\beta} < 1$. However, it should be noted that the solution for $\tilde{\beta}$ obtained from the quadratic will be a function of ϱ. Since ϱ is usually unknown, Koyck proposes scanning the entire range of ϱ. He considers the possibilities of positively autocorrelated and negatively autocorrelated disturbances separately.

Alternatively[19], one might consider the possibility of employing an estimate of ϱ and then solve the equations (2.4.17) for parameter estimates. To do so we consider $w_t = u_t - \beta u_{t-1}$ and work out under the aforementioned assumptions[20]

$$\operatorname{var} w_t = \sigma_w^2 = (1 + \beta^2 - 2\beta\varrho)\sigma_u^2, \qquad (2.4.19)$$

and

28

$$\varrho_w = \frac{\text{cov}(w_t, w_{t-1})}{\text{var } w_t} = \frac{(1 + \beta^2)\varrho - \beta - \beta\varrho^2}{1 + \beta^2 - 2\beta\varrho}, \tag{2.4.20}$$

which can also be written as

$$\beta\varrho^2 - (1 + \beta^2 + 2\beta\varrho_w)\varrho + \{\beta + (1 + \beta^2)\varrho_w\} = 0, \tag{2.4.21}$$

so that ϱ_w is the first order autocorrelation between $\{w_t\}$. Now an application of some suitable method of estimation, say Liviatan's (to be discussed below), to (2.3.5) would yield the residuals

$$\hat{w}_t = y_t - \hat{\alpha}x_t - \hat{\beta}y_{t-1}, \tag{2.4.22}$$

and then

$$\hat{\varrho}_w = \frac{\Sigma \hat{w}_t \hat{w}_{t-1}}{\Sigma \hat{w}_{t-1}^2}. \tag{2.4.23}$$

Using this estimate of ϱ_w and the estimate $\hat{\beta}$ of β, the quadratic equation (2.4.21) would yield two estimates of ϱ.[21] The value of ϱ satisfying the condition $|\varrho| < 1$ could now be used in deriving Koyck's estimates as suggested above.[22] It is evident that if a consistent estimate of ϱ is inserted into (2.4.17), Koyck's estimates will remain consistent.

Klein's Estimation Method

In trying to develop the ideas of Koyck, Klein illustrates how the 'reduced' form (2.3.5) can be viewed as a model with observed variables subject to observation error and proposes an alternative way of arriving at the Koyck's estimates $\tilde{\alpha}$ and $\tilde{\beta}$. An outline of his procedure is given below. Rewriting (2.3.5) as

$$(y_t - u_t) = \alpha x_t + \beta(y_{t-1} - u_{t-1}), \tag{2.4.24}$$

we can interpret this equation as an 'error in variables' model. In this form u_t may be treated as an error in y_t and u_{t-1} as an error in y_{t-1}, while there is no error in the equation. By writing η_t for the 'systematic' or 'true' part of y_t the errors in the variables can be expressed as

$$u_t = y_t - \alpha x_t - \beta\eta_{t-1}$$

and $\tag{2.4.25}$

$$u_{t-1} = y_{t-1} - \eta_{t-1}, \quad \eta_t \overset{\text{def}}{=} \alpha \sum_{j=0}^{\infty} \beta^j x_{t-j},$$

where the symbol $\overset{\text{def}}{=}$ denotes equality by definition. For estimation purposes two cases will be distinguished:

a. Non-autocorrelated disturbances $(Eu_t u_{t'} = 0, t' \neq t)$

This assumption implies that the two errors u_t and u_{t-1} are uncorrelated. Further, u_t is independent of $(y_t - u_t)$ and u_{t-1} is independent of $(y_{t-1} - u_{t-1})$. With an added assumption of normality of the errors it is well known that the maximum likelihood estimators of α and β depend on the ratio of the error variances.[23] In this particular situation we have

$$\text{var } u_t = \text{var } u_{t-1},$$

in accordance with the assumption of homoscedasticity of variances. Therefore, a suggestion is to minimize the sum

$$\Sigma u_t^2 + \Sigma u_{t-1}^2 \tag{2.4.26}$$

or

$$\Sigma(y_t - \alpha x_t - \beta \eta_{t-1})^2 + \Sigma(y_{t-1} - \eta_{t-1})^2 \tag{2.4.27}$$

with respect to α, β and each η_t, $t = 1, \ldots, T$. The set of normal equations so obtained will lead to the estimates of α and β which are identical with those derived from the two normal equations proposed by Koyck in case of zero autocorrelation. However, this system of normal equations is cumbersome and involves large algebraic manipulations in order to get the solution. An alternative and less cumbersome procedure to obtain Klein's estimates is to minimize the function

$$\omega = \frac{1}{1 + \beta^2} \, \Sigma(y_t - \alpha x_t - \beta y_{t-1})^2 \tag{2.4.28}$$

with respect to α and β. The normal equations are

$$\Sigma x_t(y_t - \tilde{\alpha} x_t - \tilde{\beta} y_{t-1}) = 0 \tag{2.4.29}$$

and

$$\tilde{\beta} \, \Sigma(y_t - \tilde{\alpha} x_t - \tilde{\beta} y_{t-1})^2 + (1 + \tilde{\beta}^2) \, \Sigma y_{t-1}(y_t - \tilde{\alpha} x_t - \tilde{\beta} y_{t-1}) = 0. \tag{2.4.30}$$

Solving (2.4.29) for $\tilde{\alpha}$ in terms of $\tilde{\beta}$ we get

$$\tilde{\alpha} = c_1 - \tilde{\beta} c_2, \tag{2.4.31}$$

where

$$c_1 = \Sigma x_t y_t / \Sigma x_t^2 \text{ and } c_2 = \Sigma x_t y_{t-1} / \Sigma x_t^2. \tag{2.4.32}$$

Substituting (2.4.31) and (2.4.32) into (2.4.30) and then solving for $\tilde{\beta}$ we readily obtain the quadratic equation

$$\tilde{\beta}^2(c_1 \Sigma x_t y_{t-1} - \Sigma y_t y_{t-1}) + \tilde{\beta}(\Sigma y_t^2 - \Sigma y_{t-1}^2 + c_2 \Sigma x_t y_{t-1} - $$
$$ - c_1 \Sigma x_t y_t) - (c_1 \Sigma x_t y_{t-1} - \Sigma y_t y_{t-1}) = 0, \tag{2.4.33}$$

as given by Klein. The estimates of α and β thus obtained are identical with those of Koyck and, therefore, consistent.

Their asymptotic covariance matrix is given by

$$
\operatorname*{plim}_{T \to \infty} T
\begin{bmatrix} x'_{**}x_{**} & x'_{**}\eta_* \\ x'_{**}\eta_* & \eta'_*\eta_* \end{bmatrix}^{-1}
\begin{bmatrix} x'_{**}Wx_{**} & x'_{**}W\eta_* \\ x'_{**}W\eta_* & \eta'_*W\eta_* + T\left(\dfrac{1-\beta^2}{1+\beta^2}\right)^2\sigma_u^4 \end{bmatrix}
$$

$$
\begin{bmatrix} x'_{**}x_{**} & x'_{**}\eta_* \\ x'_{**}\eta_* & \eta'_*\eta_* \end{bmatrix}^{-1} ,
\tag{2.4.34}
$$

where

$$
x_{**} = \begin{bmatrix} x_2 \\ \vdots \\ x_T \end{bmatrix}, \quad \eta_* = \begin{bmatrix} \eta_1 \\ \vdots \\ \eta_{T-1} \end{bmatrix},
\tag{2.4.35}
$$

η_t is defined in (2.4.25) and

$$
W = \sigma_u^2
\begin{bmatrix}
1+\beta^2 & -\beta & 0 & \cdots & 0 & 0 \\
-\beta & 1+\beta^2 & -\beta & & 0 & 0 \\
0 & -\beta & & & & 0 \\
\vdots & & & & & \\
0 & & & & & -\beta \\
0 & 0 & & & -\beta & 1+\beta^2
\end{bmatrix}
\tag{2.4.36}
$$

represents the covariance matrix of $\{w_t\}$ when $\{u_t\}$ are independent. The latter procedure is due to Amemiya and Fuller (1967). They have also shown that Klein's estimator is asymptotically less efficient as compared with the maximum likelihood estimator.

From the foregoing discussion we gather that the only advantage of Klein's approach is that it presents an alternative interpretation of Koyck's model and shows that it is no longer necessary to compute OLS estimates of (2.3.5) in order to arrive at Koyck's estimates in the case $\varrho = 0$.

b. Autocorrelated disturbances $(Eu_t u_{t'} = \varrho^{\,|\,t-t'\,|}\,\sigma_u^2)$

Recall that the above analysis is based on the independence of $\{u_t\}$, that is $\varrho = 0$. In most cases, this has proved to be a too restrictive assumption. Klein, therefore, attempts to generalize the analysis by including the case that $\{u_t\}$ are autocorrelated as specified in Assumption 4 given above. In that case the model (2.4.24) will be transformed into

$$
(y'_t - e_t) = \alpha\, x'_t + \beta\,(y'_{t-1} - e_{t-1}),
\tag{2.4.37}
$$

31

where $y_t' = y_t - \varrho y_{t-1}$ and $x_t' = x_t - \varrho x_{t-1}$. Further, if $\{e_t\}$ are normal in addition to their properties of statistical independence and identical distribution, the minimization of the function

$$\Sigma e_t^2 + \Sigma e_{t-1}^2$$

with respect to α, β, ϱ and each η_t in the same way as above will result in a set of normal equations. After simplification two of the four equations will be similar to those given in (2.4.31) and (2.4.33). The only change will be in the nature of the variables entering therein. Instead of the original variables y_t, x_t etc., now transformed variables y_t', x_t' etc. will occur. For reference purposes let us call these equations by (2.4.31a) and (2.4.33a), respectively. The other two equations are given by

$$\eta_{t-1}' = (y_{t-1}' + \beta y_t' - \alpha\beta x_t') / (1 + \beta^2) \qquad (2.4.38)$$

and

$$\varrho = p/q, \qquad (2.4.39)$$

where

$$p = \Sigma(y_{t-1} - \eta_{t-1}') y_{t-2} - \Sigma(y_t - \alpha x_t - \beta\eta_{t-1}') (\alpha x_{t-1} - y_{t-1}),$$
$$q = \Sigma(\alpha x_{t-1} - y_{t-1})^2 + \Sigma y_{t-2}^2.$$

Unfortunately, these equations are highly non-linear in unknown parameters. Therefore, the solution can be obtained only by iterations. (i) Assume a value of ϱ over the range $(-1, 1)$ and obtain the transformed variables y_t', x_t', ... (ii) Using the quadratic (2.4.33a) derive an initial estimate of β such that $0 \leqslant \beta < 1$. The corresponding estimate of α is computed from (2.4.31a). (iii) Next, construct observations on η_{t-1}' for each time period by means of the equation (2.4.38) and then a new estimate of ϱ is derived by using (2.4.39). The steps can now be repeated. Klein proposes to employ an OLS estimate of ϱ in the initial stage in order to get the transformed model (2.4.37). As we have already pointed out (cf. Chapter 1), the difficulty with this procedure is that it does not guarantee the consistency of the final estimates to which the iterative procedure would converge.

Liviatan's Consistent Estimator

Having recognized the fact that both Koyck and Klein have failed to provide a satisfactory solution of the estimation problem in the case $\{u_t\}$ are correlated in successive time periods, Liviatan proposed the following rather simple instrumental variables method which yields consistent

32

estimates of the parameters α and β in the distributed lag model (2.3.5). The method is independent of the autocorrelation properties of the disturbances.

The first step of the estimation procedure is to choose a $(T-1) \times 2$ matrix, say Ψ, of observations on the instruments (equal to the number of parameters to be estimated) such that for $T \to \infty$

$$\text{plim}\,(\Psi'w_{**}/T) = 0$$

and $\hspace{9cm}$ (2.4.40)

$$\text{plim}\,(\Psi'Z/T) \text{ exists and is non-singular,}$$

where

$$w_{**} = y_{**} - \alpha x_{**} - \beta y_*, \; y_{**} = \begin{bmatrix} y_2 \\ \vdots \\ y_T \end{bmatrix}, \; y_* = \begin{bmatrix} y_1 \\ \vdots \\ y_{T-1} \end{bmatrix}, \hspace{1cm} (2.4.41)$$

$$Z = (x_{**} \quad y_*),$$

x_{**} being introduced in (2.4.35). Such a matrix can be constructed with the help of observations on some or all of the independent (non-stochastic and fixed) variables and/or of constant numbers. For example, in this particular situation Ψ may be chosen as

$$\Psi = \begin{bmatrix} x_2 & x_1 \\ \vdots & \vdots \\ x_T & x_{T-1} \end{bmatrix}. \hspace{3cm} (2.4.42)$$

Next, we multiply both sides of (2.3.5) successively by the 'instruments' x_t and x_{t-1}; then, summing over t from 2 through T will directly result in the following normal equations:

$$\begin{aligned} \Sigma y_t x_t &= \hat{\alpha} \Sigma x_t^2 + \hat{\beta} \Sigma x_t y_{t-1} \\ \Sigma y_t x_{t-1} &= \hat{\alpha} \Sigma x_t x_{t-1} + \hat{\beta} \Sigma x_{t-1} y_{t-1}, \end{aligned} \hspace{2cm} (2.4.43)$$

where $\Sigma x_t w_t$ and $\Sigma x_{t-1} w_t$ have been dropped because of Assumption 2, namely that x_t and w_t are uncorrelated for all t. The system (2.4.43) leads to

$$\hat{\alpha} = \frac{1}{\Delta}(\Sigma x_t y_t \cdot \Sigma x_{t-1} y_{t-1} - \Sigma x_t y_{t-1} \cdot \Sigma x_{t-1} y_t), \hspace{1cm} (2.4.44)$$

and

$$\hat{\beta} = \frac{1}{\Delta}(\Sigma x_t^2 \cdot \Sigma x_{t-1} y_t - \Sigma x_t x_{t-1} \cdot \Sigma x_t y_t), \hspace{1cm} (2.4.45)$$

33

where

$$\Delta = \Sigma x_t^2 \cdot \Sigma x_{t-1} y_{t-1} - \Sigma x_t x_{t-1} \cdot \Sigma x_t y_{t-1}, \qquad (2.4.46)$$

provided, $\Delta \neq 0$. Since x_t and y_t are assumed to be measured from their respective means and Δ can be written as

$$\Delta = \Sigma x_t^2 (\Sigma x_{t-1}^2 \Sigma y_{t-1}^2)^{\frac{1}{2}} \, (r_{y_{t-1}, x_{t-1}} - r_{y_{t-1}, x_t} r_{x_t, x_{t-1}}), \qquad (2.4.47)$$

where rs within parentheses denote sample correlations between their indexed variables, the above condition implies that the partial correlation (*sample*) between y_{t-1} and the 'proper' instrument[24] x_{t-1} after the influence of x_t has been eliminated is not equal to zero. The corresponding condition for the estimates $\hat{\alpha}$ and $\hat{\beta}$ to be consistent is that the partial correlation (*population*) between y_{t-1} and x_{t-1} ignoring the effect of x_t is not zero. This condition is likely to hold in any practical situation.

In order to examine its consistency consider the estimates given by (2.4.44) to (2.4.46) in the matrix notation;

$$\begin{pmatrix} \hat{\alpha} \\ \hat{\beta} \end{pmatrix} = (\Psi'Z)^{-1}\Psi'y_{**}. \qquad (2.4.48)$$

The sampling error is

$$\begin{pmatrix} \hat{\alpha} - \alpha \\ \hat{\beta} - \beta \end{pmatrix} = (\Psi'Z)^{-1}\Psi'w_{**}. \qquad (2.4.49)$$

Evaluating its probability limit, we notice that

$$\underset{T \to \infty}{\text{plim}} \, (\Psi'w_{**}/T) = \underline{0}, \qquad (2.4.50)$$

because the elements of the matrix Ψ are uncorrelated with those of w_{**}. Since, by assumption, $\underset{T \to \infty}{\text{plim}}(\Psi'Z/T)^{-1}$ is a finite non-singular matrix, we conclude that $\hat{\alpha}$ and $\hat{\beta}$ are consistent.

Although Liviatan's estimates are consistent and simple to compute, these are found to be of limited importance in empirical applications. In a recent Monte Carlo experiment Morrison (1970) concludes that the precision of Liviatan's estimates may be considerably low with β approaching unity except for sufficiently large sample sizes. Nevertheless, the claim that Liviatan's estimator is consistent even when some of the regressors in the model are stochastic makes it interesting and useful in econometric analysis. According to Hannan (1965, p. 215), the asymptotic distribution of

34

the estimator is normal. As regards its finite sample properties we shall give a detailed account in the next chapter.

Hannan and Amemiya-Fuller Estimators

As we have analyzed, Liviatan's method will not be free of troubles if either the sample size is small or β is close to unity. Moreover, the choice of the instruments will always be arbitrary, which has an important bearing on the efficiency of the estimates. In order to gain greater precision in the estimation of α and β, Hannan employs an alternative technique for estimating (2.3.4). He, in fact, considers a slightly different model, namely,

$$y_t = \text{constant} + \alpha \sum_{j=0}^{\infty} \beta^j x_{t-j} + u_t, \qquad |\beta| < 1 \qquad (2.4.51)$$

where $\{u_t\}$ are assumed to be generated linearly by a general moving average process

$$u_t = \sum_{-\infty}^{\infty} \alpha_j e_{t-j}, \qquad \sum_{-\infty}^{\infty} |\alpha_j| < \infty \qquad (2.4.52)$$

and $\{e_t\}$ are temporally independent and identically distributed with finite moments through the fourth order.

His analysis draws upon the theory of spectral techniques and is in the frequency domain. The normal equations he derives [given in equation (4.3) of his article] are non-linear in parameters. In order to solve them an iterative procedure has been outlined which requires an initial estimate of β by Liviatan's consistent method. Hannan shows that the estimator converges in the limit to a normal distribution and is asymptotically more efficient than Liviatan's estimator. However, a severe limitation of the number of time series observations restricts the use of this estimator in practice.

Subsequently, Amemiya and Fuller show that Hannan's estimator is asymptotically Aitken's generalized least squares estimator or equivalently maximum likelihood estimator (when $\{e_t\}$ are normally distributed). In the time domain Hannan's estimator of (2.3.5) based on T observations on x_t and y_t is approximately[25]

$$\begin{pmatrix} \bar{\alpha} \\ \bar{\beta} \end{pmatrix} = \left[\begin{pmatrix} x'_{**} \\ \frac{1}{\alpha}\eta'_* \end{pmatrix} W^{-1} (x_{**} \quad y_*) \right]^{-1} \begin{pmatrix} x'_{**} \\ \frac{1}{\alpha}\eta'_* \end{pmatrix} W^{-1} y_{**}, \qquad (2.4.53)$$

where

$$W = E w_{**} w'_{**}, \qquad (2.4.54)$$

35

x_{**}, η_* and w_{**}, y_{**} (each of $T-1$ elements) are defined in (2.4.35) and (2.4.41), respectively, and the parameters α and β occurring in η_t's and the covariance matrix W are replaced by their consistent estimates by Liviatan's method.

The asymptotic covariance matrix of this estimator is

$$\underset{T\to\infty}{\text{plim}} \, T \left[\begin{pmatrix} x'_{**} \\ \eta'_* \end{pmatrix} W^{-1} \, (x_{**} \quad \eta_*) \right]^{-1} \tag{2.4.55}$$

assuming, of course, that the probability limit exists. An explicit expression for W in the case $\{u_t\}$ are generated through a linear process as given in Assumption 4 can be worked out easily;

$$W = \sigma_u^2 (1-\beta\varrho)(\varrho-\beta) \begin{bmatrix} \varphi & 1 & \cdots & \varrho^{T-4} & \varrho^{T-3} \\ 1 & & & & \\ \vdots & & & & 1 \\ \varrho^{T-4} & & & & 1 \\ \varrho^{T-3} & & 1 & & \varphi \end{bmatrix} \tag{2.4.56}$$

where

$$\varphi = \frac{1+\beta^2-2\beta\varrho}{(\varrho-\beta)(1-\beta\varrho)}. \tag{2.4.57}$$

An important conclusion of their analysis is that if some of the regressors in the model are lagged dependent variables, as in the present case, the efficiency of Aitken's estimator derived by substituting consistent estimate of W in (2.4.53) may be far less than that obtained on the basis of the true value of the covariance matrix W, the more so according as β is nearer to unity. Lastly, the authors propose an alternative estimator of (2.3.4). The method is based on the Gauss-Newton estimation procedure in a non-linear regression model and converges asymptotically to the maximum likelihood estimator.

Dhrymes' Search Technique

More recently Dhrymes (1969) while dealing with the problem of estimation of distributed lags has considered a more general form of the model (2.3.4), namely

$$y_t = \alpha_1 \sum_{j=0}^{\infty} \beta^j x_{t-j,\,1} + \sum_{i=2}^{n} \alpha_i x_{ti} + u_t, \quad 0 < |\beta| < 1 \tag{2.4.58}$$

36

which includes more than one explanatory variable and only the first of which, x_{t1}, is assumed to be subject to an infinite lag scheme.

For a given sample of T observations the above model can also be written as

$$y_t = \alpha_1 \sum_{j=0}^{t-1} \beta^j x_{t-j,1} + \sum_{i=2}^{n} \alpha_i x_{ti} + \alpha_0 \beta^t + u_t, \quad t = 1, \ldots, T \qquad (2.4.59)$$

where

$$\alpha_0 = \alpha_1 \eta_0, \qquad (2.4.60)$$

$$\eta_0 = \sum_{j=0}^{\infty} \beta^j x_{-j,1} \qquad (2.4.61)$$

and η_0 is called the 'truncation remainder'. Define

$$x_{t0}^* = \beta^t$$

$$x_{t1}^* = \sum_{j=0}^{t-1} \beta^j x_{t-j,1} \qquad (2.4.62)$$

$$x_{ti}^* = x_{ti}, \qquad \begin{matrix} i = 2, 3, \ldots, n \\ t = 1, 2, \ldots, T \end{matrix}$$

so that x_{t1}^* is a composite variable, observations on which are given by

$$x_{11}^* = x_{1,1}$$
$$x_{21}^* = x_{2,1} + \beta x_{1,1}$$
$$\cdot$$
$$\cdot \qquad\qquad\qquad\qquad\qquad (2.4.63)$$
$$\cdot$$
$$x_{T1}^* = x_{T,1} + \beta x_{T-1,1} + \ldots + \beta^{T-1} x_{1,1}.$$

This enables us to express (2.4.59) in the matrix notation as

$$y = X^* \alpha^* + u, \qquad (2.4.64)$$

where

$$y = \begin{bmatrix} y_1 \\ \vdots \\ y_T \end{bmatrix} \qquad (2.4.65)$$

is the vector of observations on the dependent variable y_t,

$$X^* = \begin{bmatrix} x_{11}^* & \cdots & x_{1n}^* & x_{10}^* \\ \vdots & & & \\ x_{T1}^* & & x_{Tn}^* & x_{T0}^* \end{bmatrix} \qquad (2.4.66)$$

37

is the $T \times (n + 1)$ matrix of observations on the explanatory variables (assumed to be fixed and non-stochastic),

$$\alpha^* = \begin{bmatrix} \alpha_1 \\ \vdots \\ \alpha_n \\ \alpha_0 \end{bmatrix} \qquad (2.4.67)$$

is the coefficient vector to be estimated and u is the column vector of T disturbances. Under the Assumptions 1 through 4 given in Section 2.3 and the additional assumption of normality, the log likelihood function of the parameters may be formulated as

$$L(\alpha^*, \beta, \varrho, \sigma^2 / y\text{'s and } x\text{'s}) = -\frac{T}{2} \log 2\pi - \frac{T}{2} \log \sigma^2 -$$

$$-\frac{1}{2} \log |V| - \frac{1}{2\sigma^2} (y - X^*\alpha^*)' V^{-1} (y - X^*\alpha^*), \qquad (2.4.68)$$

where

$$E\mathbf{u}\mathbf{u}' = \sigma^2 V \text{ and } V = \frac{1}{1-\varrho^2} \begin{bmatrix} 1 & \varrho & \cdots & \varrho^{T-1} \\ \varrho & & & \\ \vdots & & & \\ \varrho^{T-1} & & & 1 \end{bmatrix} . \qquad (2.4.69)$$

Now differentiation of (2.4.68) with respect to α^*, β, ϱ and σ^2 and then equating the first order derivatives to zero, will produce normal equations which will obviously be non-linear in β and ϱ. Dhrymes has, therefore, suggested the following 'search' procedure:

Denoting the efficient estimates of α^*, β, ϱ and σ^2 by a^*, b, r and s^2, respectively, first differentiate (2.4.68) with respect to α^* and σ^2 and equating them to zero, obtain the solutions for a^* and s^2 in terms of β and ϱ. Substituting a^* and s^2, thus obtained, in (2.4.68) will give the 'concentrated' log likelihood function as

$$L(\beta, \varrho / y\text{'s and } x\text{'s}) = -\frac{T}{2} (1 + \log 2\pi) - \frac{T}{2} \log \left[\frac{s^2 (\beta, \varrho)}{(1-\varrho^2)^{1/T}} \right]. \quad (2.4.70)$$

It follows that the values of β and ϱ which globally minimize

$$s^2(\beta, \varrho)/(1-\varrho^2)^{1/T}$$
$$= (y - X^*a^*)' V^{-1} (y - X^*a^*) / [T(1-\varrho^2)^{1/T}] \qquad (2.4.71)$$

38

will provide an absolute maximum of (2.4.68). Since the ranges for β and ϱ are $0 < |\beta|, |\varrho| < 1$, the problem is thus to search for that value of (β, ϱ) over the region $(-1, 1)$ which yields global minimum of (2.4.71).

The computational procedure may now be summarized as follows: For alternative values of β and ϱ in the interval $(-1, 1)$ compute successively

(i) $a^*(\beta, \varrho) = (X^{*\prime}V^{-1}X^*)^{-1} X^{*\prime}V^{-1}y$,

(ii) $s^2(\beta, \varrho) = (y - X^*a^*)' \, V^{-1} (y - X^*a^*)/T$

$(2.4.72)$

and select that pair of (β, ϱ) which globally minimizes s^2. [26] The corresponding estimate of a^* is then given by (i) above with (β, ϱ) replaced by (b, r).

For deriving asymptotic moments of the parameter estimates define

$$X = (x_1^* \, x_2 \ldots x_n), \tag{2.4.73}$$

where

$$x_1^* = B^*x_1 = \begin{bmatrix} 1 & 0 & \cdots & 0 \\ \beta & 1 & & 0 \\ \vdots & & & \\ \beta^{T-1} & \beta^{T-2} & & 1 \end{bmatrix} \begin{bmatrix} x_{1,1} \\ x_{2,1} \\ \\ x_{T,1} \end{bmatrix} \tag{2.4.74}$$

and

$$\beta = (\beta \ \ \beta^2 \ \ \ldots \ \ \beta^T)'. \tag{2.4.75}$$

Then the approximate covariance matrix of the estimators of the parameters $(\alpha_1, \alpha_2, \ldots, \alpha_n, \alpha_0)$ is given by

$$\sigma^2(\beta, \varrho) \begin{bmatrix} X'V^{-1}X & X'V^{-1}\beta \\ \beta'V^{-1}X & \beta'V^{-1}\beta \end{bmatrix}^{-1} \tag{2.4.76}$$

and those of b and r are given by

$$\text{var }(b) =$$
$$\sigma^2 \, (\beta, \varrho) \, [\alpha_1^2 \, x_1' \, B^{**\prime} \, \{V^{-1} - V^{-1}X(X'V^{-1}X)^{-1}X'V^{-1}\} \, B^{**}x_1]^{-1} \tag{2.4.77}$$

and

$$\text{var }(r) = (1 - \varrho^2)^2 \, / \, \{T(1 - \varrho^2) + (3\varrho^2 - 1) - 2\varrho^2/T\}, \tag{2.4.78}$$

respectively, where

$$B^{**} = \frac{\partial B^*}{\partial \beta} = \begin{bmatrix} 0 & 0 & \cdots & 0 & 0 \\ 1 & 0 & & 0 & 0 \\ 2\beta & 1 & & 0 & 0 \\ \vdots & & & & \\ (T-1)\beta^{T-2} & (T-2)\beta^{T-3} & & 1 & 0 \end{bmatrix} \tag{2.4.79}$$

39

and the parameters α^*, β, ϱ and $\sigma^2(\beta, \varrho)$ are replaced by their respective efficient estimates. In particular, if $\alpha_2 = \alpha_3 = \ldots = \alpha_n = 0$, the model in (2.4.58) immediately specializes to Koyck's model (2.3.4). In that case it is easy to get an explicit expression for the variance of α_1 from (2.4.76), for then X will simply be a vector of T elements.

1. The preliminary analysis to be presented in this section is largely due to Koyck.
2. At the outset this assumption of linearity might appear to be highly restrictive but it is a common experience that several times it is possible to transform non-linear models to linear models. Moreover, linear models are not necessarily always bad approximations to the real world provided suitable ranges for the variables involved are considered (see also Chapter 1).
3. Here time is assumed to be a discrete variable. This equation may be considered as a discrete analogue of the continuous form

$$q(t) = \int_0^\infty \alpha(\tau)p(t-\tau)d\tau$$

where $p(t)$ and $q(t)$ are continuous functions of time and $\alpha(\tau)$ represents the 'weight' of the variable p at the time $(t-\tau)$.
4. The *time shape of the economic reaction of* y_t *on* x_t as described by the behaviour equation (2.2.1) is defined as the change in y_t per unit of time resulting from a change in x_t for $t = 0, 1, \ldots$.
5. For evidence consult Fisher (1937), Alt (1942), Tinbergen (1949), Koyck (1954), Nerlove (1958), Solow (1960).
6. Quoted in Nerlove (1958), pp. 9-11.
7. This is a special case of the Pascal family of lag distributions proposed by Solow (1960). See also Jorgenson (1966).
8. For simplicity sake it is assumed here that the whole distribution of lagged effects can be approximated by a geometric curve, that is from $k = 0$. This assumption implies that the impact of the most recent data on the variable 'to be explained' is the greatest while the impact of the data in the succeeding periods diminishes at an exponential rate as we move in the past.
9. We could also assume $0 \leqslant |\beta| < 1$ as our stability condition but on economic grounds the condition $0 \leq \beta < 1$ seems preferable.
10. Without any loss of generality we assume that the observable variables are measured from their respective means.
11. On the other hand one serious repercussion of Koyck's transformation is that the transformed equation contains autocorrelated errors even if the errors in the original equation are uncorrelated.
12. The symbol 'E' is the well known operator denoting mathematical expectation.
13. Throughout this section it is implied that the summation over t varies from 2 through T unless it is otherwise specified.
14. The symbol 'Σ' denotes summation with respect to t.
15. An estimator $\hat{\theta}_n$ of a parameter θ calculated from a sample of n observations is said to be *unbiased* if $E\hat{\theta}_n = \theta$ exists for all sample sizes n. If $E\hat{\theta}_n \neq \theta$, the estimator is said to be *biased*.

40

It may be positively or negatively biased according as the difference $(E\hat{\theta}_n - \theta)$ is greater or less than zero. If the bias vanishes for infinitely large n, or in symbols

$$\lim_{n \to \infty} E\hat{\theta}_n - \theta = 0,$$

we shall call $\hat{\theta}_n$ as *asymptotically unbiased*. If $\lim\limits_{n \to \infty} E\hat{\theta}_n \neq \theta$, it will be called *asymptotically biased*. Sometimes asymptotic bias of an estimator is also defined as the bias of its limiting distribution [see, for example, Koopmans and Hood (1953), p. 129].

16. 'plim' is to be read as 'the probability limit of'. *An estimator $\hat{\theta}_n$ is said to possess the probability limit θ if, for all positive ε*

$$P\,|\,\hat{\theta}_n - \theta\,| > \varepsilon$$

approaches zero as n tends to infinity. In other words this condition means that $\hat{\theta}_n$ converges in probability to θ or $\hat{\theta}_n$ is a consistent estimator of θ.

17. In practice, the consistency of an estimator $\hat{\theta}_n$ of the parameter θ is proved by establishing the following results:

(i) $\lim\limits_{n \to \infty} E\hat{\theta}_n$ and   (ii) $\lim\limits_{n \to \infty} \operatorname{var} \hat{\theta}_n$

exist and are equal to θ and zero, respectively. However, these are only sufficient conditions and are much stronger than the necessary conditions. An estimator may be consistent even if its expected value and variance do not exist. A consistent estimator may not necessarily be asymptotically unbiased. This is evident, for example, from the following frequency function of an estimator $\hat{\theta}_n$ of a parameter θ [cf. Sewell (1969)]:

$$P\{\hat{\theta}_n = \theta\} = 1 - \frac{1}{n} \quad \text{and} \quad P\{\hat{\theta}_n = n^k\} = \frac{1}{n}$$

Then

$$\operatorname*{plim}_{n \to \infty} \{\hat{\theta}_n = \theta\} = 1$$

but

$$\lim_{n \to \infty} E\hat{\theta}_n = \theta + \lim_{n \to \infty} n^{k-1}$$
$$= \theta + 1 \text{ or } \infty$$

according as $k = 1$ or $k > 1$, respectively. For further discussion of the property of consistency we refer to LeCam and Schwartz (1960) and Christ (1966), p. 263. The conditions under which the least squares estimates are acceptable, reference is made to Koopmans and Hood (1953), pp. 128-133.

18. An explicit expression of the quadratic is

$$\tilde{\beta}^2 \Delta(b - \varrho) + \tilde{\beta}\{\Delta\,(1 - b\varrho) + k(b - \varrho) - \Sigma x_t^2\,\Sigma\dot{w}_t^2\} +$$
$$+ \{k(1 - b\varrho) + \varrho\Sigma x_t^2\,\Sigma\dot{w}_t^2\} = 0,$$

where $k = \Sigma x_t y_t\,\Sigma x_t y_{t-1} - \Sigma x_t^2 \Sigma y_t y_{t-1}$, $\Delta = \Sigma x_t^2 \Sigma y_{t-1}^2 - (\Sigma x_t y_{t-1})^2$.

19. We may call this method as '*Modified Koyck Procedure*'.

20. Another approach would be to estimate u_t from the relationship $u_t = \beta u_{t-1} + w_t$ (assuming $u_0 = 0$) and then employ $\varrho = \Sigma u_t u_{t-1}\,/\,\Sigma u_t^2$ to get an estimate of ϱ.

21. In order to show that both the roots of (2.4.21) are real, consider its 'discriminant' function. Its value is given by

$$D^2 = (1 + \beta^2 + 2\beta\varrho_w)^2 - 4\beta\{\beta + (1 + \beta^2)\varrho_w\}$$
$$= (1 - \beta^2)^2 + 4\beta^2\varrho_w^2 > 0.$$

41

22. Any particular situation might result in both the roots satisfying $|\varrho| < 1$. Then the pair of values of (β, ϱ) yielding a smaller sum of squares of disturbances in (2.3.5), would be retained.

23. For proof see Johnston (1963, p. 152).

24. By a *proper* instrumental variable we mean that instrumental variable which does not enter the system being estimated.

25. Notice the difference in the definition of $\bar{y}_{t-1}$ as adopted by Amemiya and Fuller and that of η_{t-1} given in (2.4.25) above. The two symbols have the same meaning except for the constant multiplicative factor α, that is, $\eta_{t-1} = \alpha \bar{y}_{t-1}$.

26. In actual practice one need not carry on the computations indefinitely but only until the required accuracy is obtained.

3. Properties of the Liviatan's estimator

3.1 INTRODUCTION

The consistent methods of estimating distributed lag models which have been discussed in the preceding chapter may be classified as follows:

a. Method of instrumental variables – Liviatan's procedure
b. Two-stage procedures by Hannan and Amemiya-Fuller
c. Methods based on some 'iterative' or 'scanning' procedure – Koyck's and Dhrymes' scanning procedures and Klein's iterative procedure.

The two-stage procedure proposed by Hannan is based on consistent estimation of the parameters of (2.3.5) in the initial stage. He uses Liviatan's estimates for this purpose and then the second stage estimates are obtained. Similarly one may base the iterative procedures of Koyck and Klein also on Liviatan estimates in the first round of iteration. It is expected that this will lead to gain in efficiency of the Koyck-Klein estimates. Since Liviatan estimates provide useful starting points, it may be worthwhile to work out their small sample properties.

In this chapter we shall derive the bias, to order $1/T$ (T being the number of observations), and the moment matrix, to order $1/T^2$, of Liviatan estimator. We shall also analyze the bias, to order $1/T$, of the estimator of residual variance in (2.3.5) according to this procedure.

3.2 MATRIX FORMULATION OF THE MODEL (2.3.5)

Assuming that T observations are available on the dependent variable y_t and the independent variable x_t entering the model (2.3.5), we introduce the following vectors and matrices:

Vectors:[1]

$$x_{**} = \begin{bmatrix} x_2 \\ \vdots \\ x_T \end{bmatrix}, \quad y_{**} = \begin{bmatrix} y_2 \\ \vdots \\ y_T \end{bmatrix}, \quad u_{**} = \begin{bmatrix} u_2 \\ \vdots \\ u_T \end{bmatrix},$$

$$x_{*} = \begin{bmatrix} x_1 \\ \vdots \\ x_{T-1} \end{bmatrix}, \quad y_{*} = \begin{bmatrix} y_1 \\ \vdots \\ y_{T-1} \end{bmatrix}, \quad u_{*} = \begin{bmatrix} u_1 \\ \vdots \\ u_{T-1} \end{bmatrix} \quad (3.2.1)$$

and

$$\delta = \begin{pmatrix} \alpha \\ \beta \end{pmatrix};$$

Matrices:

$$X = (x_{**} \ x_{*}) = \begin{bmatrix} x_2 & x_1 \\ \vdots & \vdots \\ x_T & x_{T-1} \end{bmatrix} \text{ and } Z = (x_{**} \ y_{*}) = \begin{bmatrix} x_2 & y_1 \\ \vdots & \vdots \\ x_T & y_{T-1} \end{bmatrix} \quad (3.2.2)$$

Using the matrix notation introduced above, we may rewrite the model in (2.3.5) as

$$y_{**} = Z\delta + w_{**}, \quad w_{**} = u_{**} - \beta u_{*}, \quad (3.2.3)$$

and Liviatan's normal equations in (2.4.43) as

$$X'y_{**} = X'Z\hat{\delta}, \quad (3.2.4)$$

which yield

$$\hat{\delta} = \begin{pmatrix} \hat{\alpha} \\ \hat{\beta} \end{pmatrix} = (X'Z)^{-1} X'y_{**}. \quad (3.2.5)$$

We have seen that the estimator $\hat{\delta}$ of δ is consistent provided

a. $\text{cov}(w_t, x_t) = \text{cov}(w_t, x_{t-1}) = 0$

and

b. $\plim_{T \to \infty}(X'Z/T)$ exists as a non-singular matrix.

Let us now introduce the following covariance matrices of the disturbances:

$$\Omega = E(u_{*}w'_{**}) = E\{u_{*}(u_{**} - \beta u_{*})'\}, \quad (3.2.6)$$

which is the matrix of covariances of $\{u_{t-1}\}$ and $\{w_t\}$ and

$$W = E(w_{**}\, w'_{**}) = E\{(u_{**} - \beta u_*)\,(u_{**} - \beta u_*)'\} \tag{3.2.7}$$

is the covariance matrix of $\{w_t\}$ alone.

These covariance matrices may be analyzed under the following alternative specifications:

A. The disturbances in (2.3.4), viz. $\{u_t\}$, are temporally independent such that

$$\text{cov}\,(u_t, u_{t'}) = 0 \quad \text{if} \quad t \neq t',$$

B. u_t's follow a first order Markov scheme as in Assumption 4 given in Section 2.3. This specification implies that

$$Eu_{**}\, u'_{**} = \begin{bmatrix} \text{var}(u_2) & \text{cov}(u_2, u_3) & \cdots & \text{cov}(u_2, u_T) \\ \vdots & & & \\ \text{cov}(u_T, u_2) & \text{cov}(u_T, u_3) & & \text{var}(u_T) \end{bmatrix} = \sigma_u^2 R_2,$$

where

$$R_2 = \begin{bmatrix} 1 & \varrho & \cdots & \varrho^{T-2} \\ \varrho & 1 & & \varrho^{T-3} \\ \vdots & & & \\ \varrho^{T-2} & \varrho^{T-3} & & 1 \end{bmatrix};$$

and similar expressions can be obtained for $E(u_* u'_*)$, $E(u_* u'_{**})$, etc.

Under the former specification we may write (3.2.6) and (3.2.7) as

$$\Omega = \sigma_u^2\,(H' - \beta \cdot I), \tag{3.2.8}$$

where I is a $(T-1) \times (T-1)$ unit matrix, $\sigma_u^2 = \text{var}\ u_t$ as in Assumption 2, H is a $(T-1) \times (T-1)$ auxiliary unit matrix;

$$H = \begin{bmatrix} 0 & 1 & 0 & \cdots & 0 \\ 0 & 0 & 1 & & 0 \\ \vdots & & & & \\ 0 & 0 & 0 & & 1 \\ 0 & 0 & 0 & & 0 \end{bmatrix} \tag{3.2.9}$$

and

$$W = \sigma_u^2\,\{(1 + \beta^2) \cdot I - \beta\,(H + H')\}, \tag{3.2.10}$$

respectively.

In the latter case [Specification (B)] we will consider two cases when the parameter of autoregression 'ϱ' is different from 'β' and otherwise.

Case a: $\varrho \neq \beta$;

$$\Omega = \sigma_u^2 (R_1 - \beta R_2) \tag{3.2.11a}$$

and

$$W = \sigma_u^2 \{(1 + \beta^2) R_2 - \beta (R_1 + R_1')\}, \tag{3.2.12a}$$

where

$$R_1 = \begin{bmatrix} \varrho & \varrho^2 & \cdots & \varrho^{T-1} \\ 1 & \varrho & & \varrho^{T-2} \\ \vdots & & & \\ \varrho^{T-3} & \varrho^{T-4} & & \varrho \end{bmatrix} \tag{3.2.13}$$

and R_2 is defined above.

Case b: $\varrho = \beta$;

$$\Omega = (1 - \beta^2) \sigma_u^2 \begin{bmatrix} 0 & 0 & \cdots & 0 & 0 \\ 1 & 0 & & 0 & 0 \\ \beta & 1 & & 0 & 0 \\ \vdots & & & & \\ \beta^{T-3} & \beta^{T-4} & & 1 & 0 \end{bmatrix} \tag{3.2.11b}$$

and

$$W = \sigma_u^2 (1 - \beta^2) \cdot I \tag{3.2.12b}$$

For purposes of further analysis it shall be useful to introduce the following matrix the elements of which give covariances between the elements of vectors x_{**} and x_*, given in (3.2.1) and also their weighted sums:

$$Q = \begin{bmatrix} x_{**}' x_{**} & \alpha x_{**}' B x_* \\ x_*' x_{**} & \alpha x_*' B x_* \end{bmatrix}^{-1} \equiv \begin{pmatrix} q^{11} & q^{12} \\ q^{21} & q^{22} \end{pmatrix}, \tag{3.2.14}$$

where

$$B = \begin{bmatrix} 0 & 0 & 0 & \cdots & 0 \\ 0 & 1 & 0 & & 0 \\ 0 & \beta & 1 & & 0 \\ \vdots & & & & \\ 0 & \beta^{T-3} & \beta^{T-4} & & 1 \end{bmatrix} . \tag{3.2.15}$$

46

It immediately follows that

$$x'_{**}x_{**} = x_2^2 + \ldots + x_T^2,$$

$$x'_{*}x_{**} = x_1x_2 + \ldots + x_{T-1}x_T,$$

$$\alpha x'_{**}Bx_* = \alpha\{(x_2x_3 + \ldots + x_{T-1}x_T) +$$
$$+ \beta(x_2x_4 + \ldots + x_{T-2}x_T) + \ldots$$
$$+ \beta^{T-3}(x_2x_T)\},$$

$$\alpha x'_{*}Bx_* = \alpha\{(x_2^2 + \ldots + x_{T-1}^2) +$$
$$+ \beta(x_2x_3 + \ldots + x_{T-2}x_{T-1}) + \ldots$$
$$+ \beta^{T-3}(x_2x_{T-1})\}.$$

Furthermore,

$$q^{11} = \frac{\alpha}{\det Q^{-1}} x'_{*}Bx_* ,$$

$$q^{12} = -\frac{\alpha}{\det Q^{-1}} x'_{**}Bx_* ,$$

$$q^{21} = -\frac{1}{\det Q^{-1}} x'_{*}x_{**}, \tag{3.2.16}$$

$$q^{22} = \frac{1}{\det Q^{-1}} x'_{**}x_{**},$$

and

$$\det Q^{-1} = \alpha\,(x'_{**}x_{**} \cdot x'_{*}Bx_* - x'_{*}x_{**} \cdot x'_{**}Bx_*). \tag{3.2.17}$$

3.3 STATEMENT OF THEOREMS

In this section we present our results on the bias of Liviatan estimator under the assumption that $\{u_t\}$ follow a first order Markov scheme. The results on the moment matrix of Liviatan estimator and the bias of the residual variance estimator are derived under the assumption of temporal independence of u_t's.

The following theorems are derived under the assumption that the initial observation 'y_1' on the dependent variable y_t in (2.3.5) is *fixed* and *non-stochastic*.

Theorem I. Under the Assumptions 1 to 4 stated in Section 2.3, the bias, to order $1/T$, T being the number of observations, of the estimator $\hat{\delta}$ given in (3.2.5) is

$$E(\hat{\delta} - \delta) = -QX' \, \Omega \, XQ' \, \iota, \tag{3.3.1}$$

where Q, X and Ω are defined in (3.2.14), (3.2.2) and (3.2.11a) and

$$\iota = \begin{pmatrix} 0 \\ 1 \end{pmatrix} \tag{3.3.2}$$

is a column vector of two elements.

Corollary 1. If $\varrho = \beta$, the bias of Liviatan estimator $\hat{\delta}$ is given by (3.3.1) with Ω as defined in (3.2.11b).

Corollary 2. Under the Assumptions 1 to 3 and 5, the bias, to order $1/T$, of $\hat{\delta}$ is given by the expression in (3.3.1) with Ω as defined in (3.2.8).

If sample serial and autocorrelations of all orders between x's are zero, we have

$$Q = \begin{bmatrix} \sum\limits_{2}^{T} x_t^2 & 0 \\ 0 & \alpha \sum\limits_{2}^{T-1} x_t^2 \end{bmatrix}^{-1} = \frac{1}{\alpha \sum\limits_{1}^{T} x_t^2} \begin{bmatrix} \alpha & 0 \\ 0 & 1 \end{bmatrix} + o(1/T),$$

$$X' \Omega X = \sigma_u^2 \begin{bmatrix} (\varrho - \beta) \sum\limits_{2}^{T} x_t^2 & \varrho(\varrho - \beta) \sum\limits_{2}^{T-1} x_t^2 \\ (1 - \varrho\beta) \sum\limits_{2}^{T-1} x_t^2 & (\varrho - \beta) \sum\limits_{1}^{T-1} x_t^2 \end{bmatrix}$$

$$= \sigma_u^2 \sum\limits_{1}^{T} x_t^2 \begin{bmatrix} (\varrho - \beta) & \varrho(\varrho - \beta) \\ (1 - \varrho\beta) & (\varrho - \beta) \end{bmatrix} + o(1/T), \tag{3.3.3}$$

and, hence, the following result under the Assumptions *1* to *4* stated above:

48

Corollary 3. The bias of $\hat{\delta}$, to order $1/T$, given in (3.3.1), is simply

$$E(\hat{\delta} - \delta) = -\frac{\sigma_u^2(\varrho - \beta)}{\alpha^2} \cdot \frac{1}{\sum\limits_1^T x_t^2} \cdot \begin{pmatrix} \varrho\alpha \\ 1 \end{pmatrix} \tag{3.3.4}$$

The bias vanishes, to the order of $1/T$, if $\varrho = \beta$, that is, if w_t's are temporally independent.

Theorem II. Under the Assumptions 1 to 4 given in Section 2.3, the asymptotic covariance matrix of the estimator $\hat{\delta}$ around the true parameter vector δ is given by

$$\plim_{T\to\infty} T(\hat{\delta} - \delta)(\hat{\delta} - \delta)' = \plim_{T\to\infty} TQX'WXQ', \tag{3.3.5}$$

provided, of course, the $\plim\limits_{T\to\infty}$ exists and W is given in (3.2.12a).

Corollary 1. Under the assumptions of Theorem II and if $\varrho = \beta$, the asymptotic covariance matrix of the estimator $\hat{\delta}$ is given by (3.3.5) with W as defined in (3.2.12b).

Corollary 2. If the u-disturbances are temporally independent and follow a normal probability distribution with zero mean and constant variance σ_u^2, the asymptotic covariance matrix of $\hat{\delta}$ is as given by (3.3.5) with W as defined in (3.2.10).

Corollary 3. The asymptotic covariance matrix in (3.3.5) is simply

$$\sigma_u^2 \plim_{T\to\infty} T(1 - \beta^2) \frac{1}{\sum\limits_1^T x_t^2} \begin{bmatrix} 1 & 0 \\ 0 & 1/\alpha^2 \end{bmatrix}, \tag{3.3.6}$$

if all sample serial and autocorrelations between x's are zero and $\{u_t\}$ are temporally independent.

Theorem III. Under the Assumptions 1 to 3 and 5 of the preceding chapter, the moment matrix, to order $1/T^2$, of $\hat{\delta}$ is

$$E(\hat{\delta} - \delta)(\hat{\delta} - \delta)' = QX'(W + \varDelta)XQ', \tag{3.3.7}$$

where

$$\Delta = \sigma_u^4 \left[2(1 + 3\beta + 3\beta^2)\, n\, n' + \{(1 + 3\beta^2)\, n'\, n - \right.$$
$$- 4\beta\, n'H\, n\} \cdot I + (n'H\, n - \beta\, n'n)(H + H') +$$
$$+ (H + H')\, nn'(H + H') - 2\beta\{(H + I)nn'\,(H' + I) +$$
$$+ 2(H' + I)\, nn'\,(H + I)\} + (1 + 4\beta)\, H'\, nn'\, H -$$
$$\left. - (1 - 2\beta)\, H\, nn'H' \right] - y_1\,(W\, n\, a' + a\, n'W), \tag{3.3.8}$$

$$a = \begin{bmatrix} 1 \\ \beta \\ \vdots \\ \beta^{T-2} \end{bmatrix}, \tag{3.3.9}$$

W has been defined in (3.2.10), H in (3.2.9) and n is the second column of the $(T - 1) \times 2$ matrix XQ'.

Using (3.2.3) the estimated disturbance vector is

$$\hat{w}_{**} = y_{**} - Z\hat{\delta}.$$

Substituting the right hand side of (3.2.3) for y_{**} in the above equation, we obtain

$$\hat{w}_{**} = w_{**} - Z(\hat{\delta} - \delta). \tag{3.3.10}$$

If σ_w^2 is the residual variance in (2.3.5), we define

$$\text{the residual variance estimator} = \frac{1}{T - 1}\, \hat{w}'_{**}\hat{w}_{**}. \tag{3.3.11}$$

The following theorem can then be stated:

Theorem IV. Under the assumptions of Theorem III, the bias, to order $1/T$, of the residual variance estimator defined in (3.3.11) is given by

$$\frac{1}{T - 1}\, E\hat{w}'_{**}\hat{w}_{**} - \sigma_w^2 = \sigma_u^4\, \{(1 + 3\beta^2)n'n - 4\beta n'\, Hn\} +$$

$$+ \frac{1}{T}\, \{\text{tr}(\bar{Z}'\bar{Z}QX'\, W\, XQ') - 2\text{tr}(QX'\, W\, \bar{Z})\}, \tag{3.3.12}$$

where $\bar{Z} = E(Z)$ as defined in (3.7.16) below.

50

3.4 PROOF OF THEOREM I

By repeated substitutions in (2.3.5) for y_{t-1}, y_{t-2}, etc., and arranging the solution in matrix notation we can write

$$y_* = \bar{y}_* + \bar{v}_*, \tag{3.4.1}$$

where the 'systematic' part $\bar{y}_*$ of y_* is

$$\bar{y}_* = a y_1 + \alpha B x_* \tag{3.4.2}$$

and 'unsystematic' part $\bar{v}_*$ of y_* is

$$\bar{v}_* = u_* - a \, u_1, \tag{3.4.3}$$

y_1 and u_1 being the first elements of the vectors y_* and u_* defined in (3.2.1) and a and B have been defined in (3.3.9) and (3.2.15), respectively.

Combining (3.2.3) and (3.2.5) we obtain the sampling error of $\hat{\delta}$ as

$$\hat{\delta} - \delta = (X' Z)^{-1} X' w_{**}. \tag{3.4.4}$$

It has been argued by several authors in the past that the finite sample moments of $\hat{\delta}$ do not exist. Since the asymptotic distribution of the estimator $\hat{\delta}$ is multivariate normal, its moments according to Cramér (1946, Sections 27.7 and 28.4) are given by

$$E \, \hat{\delta} = \delta + 0 \, (1/T),$$

$$E (\hat{\delta} - \delta) (\hat{\delta} - \delta)' = \mathscr{V} + 0 \, (1/T^{3/2}),$$

under fairly general conditions, where $\mathscr{V} = Q X' \, W \, X Q'$ [see equation (3.3.7)]. Thus, even though the finite sample distribution of $\hat{\delta}$ does not possess the moments at all, we may obtain corrections to the moments of the limiting distribution of $\hat{\delta}$ by adopting the following procedure.

Using (3.4.1) we get

$$X' Z = Q^{-1} + D_{1/2} + D_0, \tag{3.4.5}$$

with Q as defined in (3.2.14) and

$$D_{1/2} = \begin{bmatrix} 0 & x'_{**} u_* \\ 0 & x'_* u_* \end{bmatrix} = \begin{bmatrix} x'_{**} \\ x'_* \end{bmatrix} \times [\underline{0} \quad u_*] = X' (\underline{0} \quad u_*) \tag{3.4.6}$$

and

$$D_0 = \begin{bmatrix} 0 & (y_1-u_1)\, x'_{**}a \\ 0 & (y_1-u_1)\, x'_{*}a \end{bmatrix} = \begin{bmatrix} x'_{**} \\ x'_{*} \end{bmatrix} [0 \quad (y_1-u_1)\cdot a]$$

$$= X'\, [0 \quad (y_1-u_1)\cdot a] \tag{3.4.7}$$

are 2×2 matrices.

To determine the orders in probability of the elements of $D_{1/2}$ we note that these elements are either zero or

$$x'_{**}u_* = \sum_2^T x_t u_{t-1} \quad \text{and} \quad x'_{*}u_* = \sum_2^T x_{t-1} u_{t-1}.$$

It is clear that their mean values are zero and

$$\text{var } (x'_{**}u_*) = \sigma_u^2 \sum_2^T x_t^2 \text{ and var } (x'_{*}u_*) = \sigma_u^2 \sum_2^T x_{t-1}^2.$$

Therefore, $x'_{**}u_*$ and $x'_{*}u_*$ can be at most of order $\sqrt{T}$ in probability. However, we will come across a contrary situation if x_t is defined as a trend variable, *which case is then to be excluded.*

While dealing with the matrix D_0 we observe that its elements are either zero or

$$(y_1-u_1)\, x'_{**}a = y_1 \sum_2^T \beta^{t-2}\, x_t - u_1 \sum_2^T \beta^{t-2}\, x_t,$$

and

$$(y_1-u_1)\, x'_{*}a = y_1 \sum_2^T \beta^{t-2}\, x_{t-1} - u_1 \sum_2^T \beta^{t-2}\, x_{t-1}.$$

Let us, first of all, examine the order in probability of

$$x'_{**}a = \sum_2^T \beta^{t-2}\, x_t.$$

In case x_t is just a constant (say, equal to unity) we have

$$x'_{**}a = \sum_2^T \beta^{t-2} = \frac{1 - \beta^{T-1}}{1-\beta},$$

which is obviously of a lower order than T^k for $k > 0$, because then

$$\lim_{T\to\infty} \frac{1}{T^k} \cdot \frac{1 - \beta^{T-1}}{1 - \beta} = 0.$$

52

Therefore, we might treat $x'_{**}a$ to be of be of $0(1)$. However, in general x_t is not a constant, but still it always assumes a finite value and so it is not unreasonable to assume that $x'_{**}a$ and similarly x'_*a are of order 1 in probability.

Next we observe that

$$E\{u_1(x'_{**}a)\} = 0$$

and

$$\text{var}\{u_1(x'_{**}a)\} = \sigma_u^2 \left(\sum_2^T \beta^{t-2} x_t\right)^2.$$

Since $\sum_2^T \beta^{t-2} x_t$ is of order 1, $\{u_1(x'_{**}a)\}$ is also of order 1. Similarly $\{u_1(x'_*a)\}$ is of order 1 in probability. Hence,

$$\{(y_1-u_1) x'_{**}a\} \text{ and } \{(y_1-u_1) x'_*a\}$$

are both of order one in probability.

The suffixes of the matrices $D_{1/2}$ and D_0 indicate their orders of magnitude in probability.

Now combining (3.4.4) and (3.4.5), we get

$$\hat{\delta} - \delta = (Q^{-1} + D_{1/2} + D_0)^{-1} X'w_{**} \tag{3.4.8}$$

and neglecting terms of higher order of smallness than $1/T$, we have

$$\hat{\delta} - \delta = A_{-1/2} + A_{-1}, \tag{3.4.9}$$

where

$$A_{-1/2} = QX'w_{**}, \quad A_{-1} = -QD_{1/2}QX'w_{**}, \tag{3.4.10}$$

the suffixes of A indicating the order of magnitude in probability. Thus $A_{-1/2}$ is of order $1/\sqrt{T}$ and A_{-1} is of order $1/T$ in probability.

To derive the bias of $\hat{\delta}$, to order $1/T$, we observe that the expectation of the first term on the right hand side of the equality sign in (3.4.9) is zero because X and Q are non-stochastic and $E w_{**} = \underline{0}$ according to Assumption 3. Therefore, we are required only to evaluate the expectation of the second term on the right hand side of (3.4.9). It will be useful, for this purpose, to write the $(T-1) \times 2$ matrix XQ' as

$$XQ' \equiv (m \quad n), \tag{3.4.11}$$

where m and n are the two columns of XQ'. Further, using (3.3.2) we obtain

$$XQ' \, \iota = \text{n}. \tag{3.4.12}$$

Then it can be verified that

$$EA_{-1} = -QE\,(D_{1/2}\,QX'\,w_{**}) = -QX'\,E\,(u_* \,\text{n}'\,w_{**})$$
$$= -QX'\,E\,(u_* w'_{**})\,\text{n} = -QX'\,E\,(u_* w'_{**})\,XQ'\,\iota$$
$$= -QX'\Omega XQ'\,\iota,$$

which is the expression of the bias given in (3.3.1).

3.5 PROOF OF THEOREM II

Using (3.4.9) we obtain

$$\underset{T\to\infty}{\text{plim}}\ TE\,(\hat{\delta}-\delta)\,(\hat{\delta}-\delta)' = \underset{T\to\infty}{\text{plim}}\ TQX'\,E\,(w_{**}w'_{**})\,XQ',$$

which gives the asymptotic covariance matrix of δ presented in (3.3.5).

3.6 PROOF OF THEOREM III

To derive the moment matrix, to order $1/T^2$, of $\hat{\delta}$ about the true parameter vector δ, we will have to retain terms to order $1/T^{3/2}$ in the expansion of the sampling error $\hat{\delta} - \delta$, stated in (3.4.8). In that case

$$\hat{\delta} - \delta = A_{-1/2} + A_{-1} + A_{-3/2}, \tag{3.6.1}$$

where

$$A_{-1/2} = QX'\,w_{**}$$
$$A_{-1} \ \ = -QD_{1/2}QX'\,w_{**} \tag{3.6.2}$$
$$A_{-3/2} = QD_{1/2}QD_{1/2}QX'\,w_{**} - QD_0QX'\,w_{**},$$

suffixes of A indicating the order of magnitude in probability. Therefore, to order $1/T^2$, we have

$$E\,(\hat{\delta} - \delta)\,(\hat{\delta} - \delta)' = E\,\{A_{-1/2}A'_{-1/2} + (A_{-1/2}A'_{-1} + A_{-1} \times$$
$$\times\ A'_{-1/2}) + (A_{-1/2}A'_{-3/2} + A_{-3/2}A'_{-1/2} + A_{-1}A'_{-1})\}. \tag{3.6.3}$$

The leading term on the right hand side of (3.6.3) provides the asymptotic covariance matrix of $\hat{\delta}$ as follows:

54

$$E(A_{-1/2}A'_{-1/2}) = QX' \, E(w_{**}w'_{**}) \, XQ' = QX' \, W \, XQ', \qquad (3.6.4)$$

where W is defined in (3.2.10).[2]

Considering the second and the third term on the right hand side of (3.6.3), we observe that the third term is just the transpose of the second. The second term can be written as

$$E(A_{-1/2}A'_{-1}) = -QX' \, E(w_{**}w'_{**} \, XQ' \, D'_{1/2}) \, Q'$$

$$= -QX' \, E(w_{**}w'_{**} \, \text{n} \, u'_*) \, XQ'.$$

It is then not difficult to verify that under the assumption of normality and temporal independence of $\{u_t\}$

$$E\,(w_{**}w'_{**} \, \text{n} \, u'_*) = \underline{0}$$

and, therefore,

$$E(A_{-1/2}A'_{-1}) = E(A_{-1}A'_{-1/2}) = \underline{0},$$

where $\underline{0}$ is a 2×2 null matrix.

Let us now consider terms of order $1/T^2$ on the right hand side of (3.6.3). First of all we note that

$$E\,(A_{-1/2}A'_{-3/2}) = E\,(A_{-3/2}A'_{-1/2})' \qquad (3.6.5)$$

and

$$A_{-1/2}A'_{-3/2} = QX'w_{**}w'_{**}XQ'D'_{1/2}Q'D'_{1/2}Q' - QX'w_{**}w'_{**}XQ'D'_0Q'.$$

Further, using (3.4.6) and (3.4.7)

$$A_{-1/2}A'_{-3/2} = QX'w_{**}w'_{**}XQ' \begin{pmatrix} 0 \\ \overline{u'_*} \end{pmatrix} XQ' \begin{pmatrix} 0 \\ \overline{u'_*} \end{pmatrix} XQ' -$$

$$- QX'w_{**}w'_{**}XQ' \begin{pmatrix} 0 \\ \overline{(y_1 - u_1)} \, a' \end{pmatrix} XQ';$$

the mathematical expectation of which can be written as

$$E(A_{-1/2}A'_{-3/2}) = QX' \, E(w_{**}w'_{**}\text{n}u'_*\text{n}u'_*) \, XQ' -$$

$$- QX' \, E\{w_{**}w'_{**}\text{n} \, a' \, (y_1 - u_1)\} \, XQ', \qquad (3.6.6)$$

where n is the second column of XQ' as indicated above. Expressing w_{**} in terms of u's with the help of the relationship $w_{**} = u_{**} - \beta u_*$, we write the first expectation on the right hand side of (3.6.6) as

$$E\,(w_{**}w'_{**}\text{n}u'_*\text{n}u'_*)$$

55

$$= E(u_{**}u'_{**}nu'_*nu'_*) - \beta\, E(u_{**}u'_*nu'_*nu'_*) -$$
$$- \beta\, E(u_*u'_{**}nu'_*nu'_*) + \beta^2 E(u_*u'_*nu'_*nu'_*)$$
$$= E\{u_{**}u'_* \,(u'_{**}n)\,(u'_*n)\} - \beta\, E\{u_{**}u'_*\,(u'_*n)\,(u'_*n)\} -$$
$$- \beta\, E\{u_*u'_*\,(u'_{**}n)\,(u'_*n)\} + \beta^2 E\{u_*u'_*\,(u'_*n)\,(u'_*n)\}. \tag{3.6.7}$$

For evaluation purposes we write

$$\mathrm{n} = \begin{bmatrix} n_2 \\ \vdots \\ n_T \end{bmatrix} \tag{3.6.8}$$

as the second column of XQ'. The following results can easily be derived then:

$$E\{u_{**}u'_*(u'_{**}n)\,(u'_*n)\} = \sigma_u^4\,\{nn' + Hnn'H + (n'Hn)\cdot H\} \tag{3.6.9}$$

$$E\{u_{**}u'_*(u'_*n)\,(u'_*n)\} = \sigma_u^4\,\{2Hnn' + (n'n)\cdot H\} \tag{3.6.10}$$

$$E\{u_*u'_*(u'_{**}n)\,(u'_*n)\} = \sigma_u^4\,\{(n'Hn)\cdot I + H'nn' + nn'H\} \tag{3.6.11}$$

$$E\{u_*u'_*(u'_*n)^2\} = \sigma_u^4\,\{(n'n)\cdot I + 2nn'\}. \tag{3.6.12}$$

The value of the second expectation on the right hand side of (3.6.6) is

$$W\,\mathrm{n}\,a'\,y_1, \tag{3.6.13}$$

because $E\,(w_{**}w'_{**}\mathrm{n}\,a'\,u_1)$ involves only third order moments of u_t which are zero according to Assumption 5.

Substituting (3.6.9)–(3.6.13) in (3.6.6) we have

$$E\,(A_{-1/2}A'_{-3/2}) = QX'[\sigma_u^4\,\{1 + 2\,\beta^2)\,nn' + (\beta^2\,n'n -$$
$$- \beta\,n'Hn)\cdot I + (n'Hn - \beta\,n'n)\cdot H + Hnn'\,H -$$
$$- \beta\,(2\,Hnn' + H'nn' + nn'H)\} - Wna'y_1]\,XQ'. \tag{3.6.14}$$

Lastly, we evaluate the following term (of order $1/T^2$) in (3.6.3):

$$E\,(A_{-1}A'_{-1}) = E\,(Q\,D_{1/2}\,QX'\,w_{**}w'_{**}\,XQ'\,D'_{1/2}\,Q'). \tag{3.6.15}$$

Using (3.4.6) and (3.4.11) we can write (3.6.15) as

$$E\,(A_{-1}A'_{-1}) = QX'\,E\,(u_*\,n'w_{**}w'_{**}\,n\,u'_*)\,XQ'. \tag{3.6.16}$$

Further,

$$E\,(u_*n'\,w_{**}w'_{**}\,n\,u'_*) = E\,(u_*\,n'\,u_{**}u'_{**}\,n\,u'_*) -$$

$$- \beta E (u_* \, \mathrm{n}' \, u_{**} u_*' \, \mathrm{n} \, u_*') -$$

$$- \beta E (u_* \, \mathrm{n}' \, u_* u_{**}' \, \mathrm{n} \, u_*') +$$

$$+ \beta^2 E (u_* \, \mathrm{n}' \, u_* u_*' \, \mathrm{n} \, u_*'), \tag{3.6.17}$$

or, alternatively,

$$E (u_* \, \mathrm{n}' \, w_{**} w_{**}' \, \mathrm{n} \, u_*') = E \{u_* u_*' \, (\mathrm{n}' \, u_{**}) \, (\mathrm{n}' \, u_{**})\} -$$

$$- \beta E \{u_* u_*' \, (\mathrm{n}' \, u_{**}) \, (u_*' \, \mathrm{n})\} -$$

$$- \beta E \{u_* u_*' \, (\mathrm{n}' \, u_*) \, (u_{**}' \, \mathrm{n})\} +$$

$$+ \beta^2 E \{u_* u_*' \, (\mathrm{n}' \, u_*) \, (u_*' \, \mathrm{n})\}. \tag{3.6.18}$$

Considering the right hand side expectations term by term we observe that the second expectation is equal to the third which is also equal to the third expectation on the right hand side of the second equality of (3.6.7).

The fourth expectation on the right hand side of the equality sign in (3.6.18) is equal to the fourth expectation on the right hand side of the second equality of (3.6.7).

Thus we need evaluate only the first expectation in (3.6.18), which is given by

$$E \{u_* u_*' (u_{**}' \mathrm{n})^2\} = \sigma_u^4 \{(\mathrm{n}'\mathrm{n}) \cdot I + 2H'\mathrm{n} \, \mathrm{n}' \, H\}. \tag{3.6.19}$$

Substituting (3.6.11), (3.6.12) and (3.6.19) in (3.6.16), we get

$$E(A_{-1} A_{-1}') = \sigma_u^4 \, QX' \, [\{(1 + \beta^2) \, \mathrm{n}'\mathrm{n} - 2 \, \beta \, \mathrm{n}'H\mathrm{n}\} \cdot I +$$

$$+ 2 \, H'\mathrm{n}\mathrm{n}'H + 2 \, \beta^2 \, \mathrm{n}\mathrm{n}' - 2 \, \beta \, (H'\mathrm{n}\mathrm{n}' +$$

$$+ \mathrm{n}\mathrm{n}'H)] \, XQ'. \tag{3.6.20}$$

Hence, combining (3.6.4), (3.6.5), (3.6.14) and (3.6.20) and rearranging terms we obtain the result stated in (3.3.7).

3.7 PROOF OF THEOREM IV

Substituting the value of the sampling error from (3.4.9) in (3.3.10) we get

$$\hat{w}_{**} = w_{**} - Z (A_{-1/2} + A_{-1}), \tag{3.7.1}$$

where terms of order less than $1/T$ in $(\hat{\delta} - \delta)$ have been dropped and $A_{-1/2}$, A_{-1} are defined in (3.4.10). Now in order to derive the bias, to order

57

$1/T$, of the residual variance estimator $\dfrac{1}{T-1}\,\hat{w}'_{**}\,\hat{w}_{**}$, it is sufficient to

retain terms, to order one, in $\hat{w}'_{**}\,\hat{w}_{**}$. Consider

$$\hat{w}'_{**}\,\hat{w}_{**} = w'_{**}\,w_{**} - 2w'_{**}\,ZA_{-1/2} -$$
$$- 2w'_{**}\,ZA_{-1} + A'_{-1/2}\,Z'\,Z\,A_{-1/2}. \tag{3.7.2}$$

The mathematical expectation of the leading term on the right of the equality sign in (3.7.2) is directly obtained as

$$E\,(w'_{**}\,w_{**}) = (T-1)\,(1+\beta^2)\,\sigma_u^2. \tag{3.7.3}$$

To evaluate the mathematical expectation of the second term we write

$$E\,(w'_{**}\,Z\,A_{-1/2}) = E\,\{w'_{**}\,(x_{**} \quad y_*)\,QX'\,w_{**}\},$$

$$= E\,\left\{w'_{**}\,(x_{**} \quad y_*)\,\begin{pmatrix} \mathrm{m}' \\ \mathrm{n}' \end{pmatrix}\,w_{**}\right\}$$

$$= E\,(w'_{**}\,x_{**}\,\mathrm{m}'\,w_{**}) + E\,(w'_{**}\,y_*\,\mathrm{n}'\,w_{**}), \tag{3.7.4}$$

where use has been made of the definitions of Z.

Under the assumptions of temporal independence and normal distribution of $\{u_t\}$, we have

$$E\,(w'_{**}\,x_{**}\,\mathrm{m}'\,w_{**}) = E\,(x'_{**}\,w_{**}\,w'_{**}\,\mathrm{m}) = x'_{**}\,W\,\mathrm{m}, \tag{3.7.5}$$

where W has been defined in (3.2.10) and

$$E\,(w'_{**}\,y_*\,\mathrm{n}'\,w_{**}) = E\,\{(\bar{y}_* + u_* - a\,u_1)'\,w_{**}\,w'_{**}\,\mathrm{n}\}$$

$$= \bar{y}'_*\,E\,(w_{**}\,w'_{**})\,\mathrm{n} + E\,(w'_{**}\,u_*\,w'_{**})\,\mathrm{n} -$$

$$- a'\,E\,(w_{**}\,w'_{**}\,u_1)\,\mathrm{n}$$

$$= \bar{y}'_*\,W\,\mathrm{n}, \tag{3.7.6}$$

where use has been made of (3.4.1)–(3.4.3) and the fact that $E(w'_{**}\,u_*\,w'_{**})$ and $E\,(w_{**}\,w'_{**}\,u_1)$ involve third order moments of the normal distribution which are zero according to Assumption 5.

Combining (3.7.4), (3.7.5) and (3.7.6) we get

$$E\,(w'_{**}\,Z\,A_{-1/2}) = x'_{**}\,W\,\mathrm{m} + \bar{y}'_*\,W\,\mathrm{n}. \tag{3.7.7}$$

To obtain the expected value of the third term on the right of the equality sign in (3.7.2) we use (3.2.2), (3.4.9) and write

$$E\,(w'_{**}\,Z\,A_{-1}) = -E\,\{w'_{**}\,(x_{**} \quad y_*)\,Q\,D_{1/2}\,Q\,X'\,w_{**}\}. \tag{3.7.8}$$

Substituting $X'(0 \quad u_*)$ for $D_{1/2}$ and $(m \quad n)$ for XQ', we have

$$E(w'_{**} \ Z \ A_{-1}) = -E(x'_{**}w_{**} \ m' \ u_* w'_{**} \ n) -$$
$$- E(y'_* \ w_{**} \ n'u_* w'_{**} \ n). \tag{3.7.9}$$

Now the first term on the right of the equality sign in (3.7.9) is

$$E(x'_{**} \ w_{**} \ m' \ u_* \ w'_{**} \ n) = x'_{**} \ E(w_{**} \ m' \ u_* \ w'_{**}) \ n = 0, \tag{3.7.10}$$

and the second term, after applying (3.4.1) to (3.4.3), is

$$E(w'_{**} \ y_* \ n' \ u_* \ w'_{**} \ n) \ = E(\bar{y}'_* w_{**} \ n' \ u_* w'_{**} \ n) +$$
$$+ E(w'_{**} \ u_* \ n'u_* w'_{**} n) -$$
$$- E(a'u_1 w_{**} \ n'u_* \ w'_{**} n). \tag{3.7.11}$$

Since the value of the first term on the right of the equality sign in (3.7.11) is zero due to the presence of third order moments and the third term is of smaller order than 1, we, therefore, need evaluate only the second term which is written as

$$E(w'_{**} \ u_* \ n' \ u_* \ w'_{**} \ n) \ = E(w'_{**} \ u_*n'u_*n'w_{**})$$
$$= E\{\text{tr} \ (u_*n'u_*n'w_{**}w'_{**})\},$$
$$= \text{tr} \ (E \ u_* \ n' \ u_* \ n' \ w_{**}w'_{**}). \tag{3.7.12}$$

The term within parentheses of the third equality on the right hand side of (3.7.12) has already been dealt with in (3.6.7) and so by combining (3.6.9) to (3.6.12), we obtain

$$E(w'_{**} \ u_* \ n' \ u_* \ w'_{**} \ n) = \text{tr} \ [\sigma_u^4 \ \{(\beta^2 \ n'n - \beta \ n'H \ n) \cdot I +$$
$$+ (n'H \ n - \beta \ n'n) \cdot H + (1 + 2\beta^2) \ nn' + H \ n \ n'H -$$
$$- \beta \ (2H \ nn' + H'nn' + nn'H)\}]. \tag{3.7.13}$$

Thus, (3.7.13) with a minus sign affixed before it gives the value of $E \ w'_{**}Z \ A_{-1}$ in (3.7.9), viz.,

$$E(w'_{**} \ Z \ A_{-1}) = -\sigma_u^4 \ [\{1 + (T + 1) \ \beta^2\} \ n'n +$$
$$+ n' \ H \ H \ n - (T + 3) \ \beta \ n' \ H \ n], \tag{3.7.14}$$

because $\text{tr} \ (nn' \ H) = n'H \ n$ and $\text{tr} \ H = \text{tr} \ H' = 0$.

Lastly, we consider the mathematical expectation of the fourth term on the right of the equality sign in (3.7.2). For this purpose, we first write

59

$$Z = \overline{Z} + \overline{V}, \tag{3.7.15}$$

where

$$\overline{Z} = (x_{**} \quad \overline{y}_*) \text{ and } \overline{V} = (\underline{0} \quad \overline{v}_*) \tag{3.7.16}$$

are the two matrices each of size $(T-1) \times 2$ so that

$$Z'Z = \overline{Z}'\overline{Z} + \overline{Z}'\overline{V} + \overline{V}'\overline{Z} + \overline{V}'\overline{V}. \tag{3.7.17}$$

Using (3.4.10) and replacing $Z'Z$ by the right hand expression in (3.7.17), we may write the fourth expectation as

$$E(A'_{-1} Z' Z A_{-1}) = E(w'_{**} X Q' \overline{Z}'\overline{Z} Q X' w_{**}) +$$
$$+ 2 E(w'_{**} X Q' \overline{Z}'\overline{V} Q X' w_{**}) +$$
$$+ E(w'_{**} X Q' \overline{V}'\overline{V} Q X' w_{**}). \tag{3.7.18}$$

It immediately follows that

$$E(w'_{**} X Q' \overline{Z}'\overline{Z} Q X' w_{**}) = \text{tr}(\overline{Z}'\overline{Z} Q X' W X Q'), \tag{3.7.19}$$

$$E(w'_{**} X Q' \overline{Z}'\overline{V} Q X' w_{**}) = 0 \tag{3.7.20}$$

and

$$E(w'_{**} X Q' \overline{V}'\overline{V} Q X' w_{**})$$

$$= E\left\{ w'_{**} (\text{m n}) \begin{pmatrix} 0 \\ \overline{v}'_* \end{pmatrix} (\underline{0} \quad \overline{v}_*) \begin{pmatrix} \text{m}' \\ \text{n}' \end{pmatrix} w_{**} \right\}$$

$$= E(w'_{**} \text{n} \, \overline{v}'_* \overline{v}_* \, \text{n}' \, w_{**}). \tag{3.7.21}$$

Furthermore,

$$E(w'_{**} \text{n} \, \overline{v}'_* \, \overline{v}_* \, \text{n}' \, w_{**}) = E(w'_{**} \text{n} \, u'_* \, u_* \, \text{n}' \, w_{**})$$
$$= \text{tr}(E \, u_* \, \text{n}' \, w_{**} \, w'_{**} \, \text{n} \, u'_*), \tag{3.7.22}$$

where we observe that the value of the term within the brackets can be obtained by combining (3.6.11), (3.6.12) and (3.6.19). Accordingly,

$$E(w'_{**} \text{n} \, \overline{v}'_* \, \overline{v}_* \, \text{n}' \, w_{**}) = \sigma_u^4 \, \text{tr} \, [\{(1 + \beta^2) \, \text{n}' \, \text{n} -$$
$$- 2 \beta \, \text{n}' H \, \text{n}\} \cdot I + 2 \, H' \text{n} \, \text{n}' \, H +$$
$$+ 2 \beta^2 \, \text{n} \, \text{n}' - 2 \beta \, (H' \text{n} \, \text{n}' + \text{n} \, \text{n}' \, H)]$$
$$= \sigma_u^4 \, [\{(T-1) + (T+1) \, \beta^2\} \, \text{n}' \, \text{n} +$$
$$+ 2 \, \text{n}' \, H \, H' \text{n} - 2 \beta \, (T+1) \, \text{n}' H \, \text{n}], \tag{3.7.23}$$

which is the value of the third term on the right of the equality sign in (3.7.18).

Therefore, combining (3.7.18), (3.7.19) and (3.7.23), we get

$$E(A'_{-1} Z' Z A_{-1}) = \text{tr}(\overline{Z}'\overline{Z} Q X' W X Q') +$$
$$+ \sigma_u^4 [\{(T-1) + (T+1) \beta^2\} \text{n}' \text{n} +$$
$$+ 2 \text{n}' H H' \text{n} - 2\beta (T+1) \text{n}' H \text{n}]. \qquad (3.7.24)$$

Hence, combining (3.7.2), (3.7.3), (3.7.7), (3.7.14) and (3.7.24), we obtain

$$E(\hat{w}'_{**} \hat{w}_{**}) = (T-1)(1+\beta^2) \sigma_u^2 + \text{tr}(\overline{Z}'\overline{Z} Q X' W X Q') -$$
$$- 2 (x'_{**} W \text{m} + \overline{y}'_* W \text{n}) +$$
$$+ \sigma_u^4 \{(T+1)(1+3\beta^2) \text{n}' \text{n} + 2 \text{n}' H(H+H') \text{n} -$$
$$- 4(T+2) \beta \text{n}' H \text{n}\}$$
$$= (T-1)(1+\beta^2) \sigma_u^2 + \text{tr}(\overline{Z}'\overline{Z} Q X' W X Q') -$$
$$- 2 \text{tr}(Q X' W \overline{Z}) +$$
$$+ \sigma_u^4 \{(T+1)(1+3\beta^2) \text{n}' \text{n} + 2 \text{n}' H(H+H') \text{n} -$$
$$- 4(T+2) \beta \text{n}' H \text{n}\}. \qquad (3.7.25)$$

Finally, dividing (3.7.25) by $(T-1)$ throughout and retaining terms to order $1/T$, we get the result stated in Theorem IV in Section 3.3.

NOTES

1. It should be noted that the vectors having x_2, y_2 or u_2 as the first element are identified with a suffix '**' and those having x_1, y_1 or u_1 as the first element with '*' as the suffix. All these vectors have T-1 elements. Furthermore, some of the vectors and matrices already defined in the preceding chapter are reproduced here for clarity sake.
2. The only difference between this result and the result stated in Theorem II (cf. Section 3.5) lies in the definition of W. In the former case W is given by (3.2.10) under the assumption of temporal independence of $\{u_t\}$, whereas in the latter it is given by (3.2.12a), which is based on the assumption that $\{u_t\}$ are autocorrelated.

4. An iterative instrumental variables estimator of (2.3.5)

4.1 INTRODUCTION

From our preceding discussion of different methods of estimation of the distributed lag model (2.3.4) it is apparent that the instrumental variables procedure is the simplest of all consistent methods. More advantageous is the fact that it is the only method which does not require an initial approximation to the parameter estimates. However, the procedure results in estimates of low precision which may be attributed to the following two main reasons:

a. arbitrary selection of instruments

b. autocorrelation properties of the composite disturbances $\{w_t\}$.

In order to obtain parameter estimates of greater precision one may proceed on the lines Hannan or Amemiya-Fuller or Dhrymes has suggested; or, alternatively, a natural approach would be to use the set of 'optimal' instruments and include the effects of the correlation properties of the disturbances in Liviatan's estimation procedure.

In the present chapter we shall develop the latter approach under the assumption that the first observation y_1 of the dependent variable y is fixed and non-stochastic. Section 2 describes the estimator and in Section 3 a numerical illustration is presented for estimating the coefficients of the model (2.3.4) according to alternative methods.

4.2 THE ESTIMATOR

Let us consider the estimator given by (2.4.48), where we know that Ψ is a matrix of instruments such that it is uncorrelated with the disturbance vector w_{**} and is highly correlated with the matrix of explanatory variables Z (of rank 2) entering the model. With respect to the disturbances we assume here

$$Ew_{**}w'_{**} = W, \qquad (4.2.1)$$

a symmetric and positive definite matrix of order $(T-1)$. In particular, W may be assumed as given by (2.4.56).

Now in accordance with the theory underlying the method of generalized least squares (GLS), the objective, as proposed by Sargan (1958, Section 4), is to choose Ψ in such a way as to minimize

$$\text{tr } E(\Psi' w_{**}w'_{**}\Psi) = \text{tr}(\Psi' W \Psi). \qquad (4.2.2)$$

Next, consider a linear transformation of the matrix Ψ, say

$$\Phi = \Psi T, \qquad (4.2.3)$$

where T is a non-singular matrix of order 2×2. Substituting Φ for Ψ in (2.4.48), we observe that the estimator $\hat{\delta}$ of δ remains unchanged. Similarly, it is easy to verify that the asymptotic covariance matrix given by (3.3.5) – with X replaced by Ψ – is invariant under a non-singular transformation of Ψ. It follows that Ψ can be transformed linearly but otherwise arbitrarily *without affecting the results essentially*. Therefore, at least one normalizing constraint should be imposed. For the latter we may choose

$$\text{tr }\{(\Psi' \bar{Z})(\Psi' \bar{Z})'\} = \text{tr } I = 2, \qquad (4.2.4)$$

being equal to the number of instruments, where

$$\bar{Z} = EZ = (x_{**} \quad Ey_*) \quad \text{[cf. equation (2.4.41)].} \qquad (4.2.5)$$

Thus the objective function to be minimized is

$$F = \text{tr}(\Psi' W \Psi) + \lambda\{2 - \text{tr}(\Psi' \bar{Z}\bar{Z}'\Psi)\}, \qquad (4.2.6)$$

λ being a Lagrange multiplier. The first order conditions for minimum F are

$$\frac{\partial F}{\partial \Psi} = 2\,W\Psi - 2\,\lambda\,\bar{Z}\bar{Z}'\Psi = \underline{0},$$

and $\qquad (4.2.7)$

$$\frac{\partial F}{\partial \lambda} = 2 - \text{tr}(\Psi' \bar{Z}\bar{Z}'\Psi) = 0.$$

Notice that the second condition is simply the constraint (4.2.4) and from the first condition we have

$$(W - \lambda\,\bar{Z}\bar{Z}')\Psi = \underline{0}, \qquad (4.2.8)$$

or

$$(W^{-1}\bar{Z}\bar{Z}' - \mu I)\Psi = \underline{0}, \tag{4.2.9}$$

where $\mu = 1/\lambda$. It follows that, first, a necessary and sufficient condition to have a nontrivial solution is that

$$| W^{-1}\bar{Z}\bar{Z}' - \mu I | = 0, \tag{4.2.10}$$

and, second, μ (or $1/\lambda$) is a characteristic root of the matrix $W^{-1}\bar{Z}\bar{Z}'$. Since, both W and $\bar{Z}\bar{Z}'$ are real and symmetric; and, further, because W is positive definite and $\bar{Z}\bar{Z}'$ is positive semidefinite (of rank 2), the roots of the polynomial equation (4.2.10) are real and non-negative. Furthermore, only 2 of the $(T-1)$ roots of the matrix $W^{-1}\bar{Z}\bar{Z}'$ are non-zero. Corresponding to each of these positive roots, there is a solution of (4.2.8) or (4.2.9) which is relevant for our purposes. Suppose, μ_i $(i = 1,2)$ is one of such roots and ξ_i its associated characteristic vector, then we can write

$$(W^{-1}\bar{Z}\bar{Z}' - \mu_i I)\,(a_i\xi_i \quad b_i\xi_i) = \underline{0}, \quad i = 1,2 \tag{4.2.11}$$

where a_i and b_i are any different scalars $\neq 0$. It suggests that the matrix Ψ may consist of the two columns given by $a_i\xi_i$ and $b_i\xi_i$. In what follows, there is a vast collection of instrumental variables out of which we must choose the set which minimizes the function F and satisfies the constraint (4.2.4). For solving the equations (4.2.4) and (4.2.8) we premultiply the latter equation by Ψ' and then take the trace throughout;

$$\lambda \operatorname{tr}(\Psi'\bar{Z}\bar{Z}'\Psi) = \operatorname{tr}(\Psi' W\Psi).$$

Further, applying the constraint (4.2.4) we get

$$\lambda = \frac{1}{2}\operatorname{tr}(\Psi' W\Psi) > 0. \tag{4.2.12}$$

Now (4.2.8) can be written as

$$\Psi = (W^{-1}\bar{Z})\,(\bar{Z}'\Psi\,\Delta), \tag{4.2.13}$$

where Δ is a 2×2 diagonal matrix having λ (given by (4.2.12)) as its diagonal elements. Since the matrix within the latter parenthesis on the right of the equality sign in (4.2.13) is non-singular, Ψ may be considered as a linear transformation of the matrix $W^{-1}\bar{Z}$. Thus,

$$\Psi = W^{-1}\bar{Z} \tag{4.2.14}$$

is accepted as a basic solution of the above function. With this value of Ψ the equation (4.2.12) yields

64

$$\lambda = \frac{1}{2} \text{ tr } (\overline{Z}' W^{-1} \overline{Z}) > 0. \tag{4.2.15}$$

Now W and $\overline{Z}$ depend on the values of α, β and ϱ which are unknown. However, we know that Liviatan's formula provides estimates of these parameters such that

$$\hat{\alpha} - \alpha = 0(1/\sqrt{T}), \quad \hat{\beta} - \beta = 0\,(1/\sqrt{T}) \quad \text{and} \quad \hat{\varrho} - \varrho = 0\,(1/\sqrt{T}).$$

Thus we can obtain $\hat{\overline{Z}}$ and $\hat{W}$ which, in the limit, converge to $\overline{Z}$ and W, respectively. Let us, therefore, work with

$$\Psi = \hat{W}^{-1} \hat{\overline{Z}}, \tag{4.2.16}$$

and when substituted into (2.4.48) we get

$$\hat{\delta} = (\hat{\overline{Z}}' \hat{W}^{-1} Z)^{-1} \hat{\overline{Z}}' \, \hat{W}^{-1} y_{**}. \tag{4.2.17}$$

Note the difference between the estimator in (4.2.17) and Hannan's estimator given by (2.4.54). The two are approximately same. These differ because in the former case the elements of the second column of $\overline{Z}$ contain the parameter α as a multiplicative constant factor while in the latter case they do not. The procedure can now be iterated. Start with an initial value, say Ψ_0, of the matrix Ψ selected in accordance with the requirements stated in (2.4.40). Using Ψ_0 for Ψ, obtain an initial estimate $\hat{\delta}_0$ of δ by means of (2.4.48); thereafter an estimate of ϱ is obtained as suggested in Section 2.4. Having got initial estimates of α, β and ϱ, a new matrix, say Ψ_1, of Ψ is constructed with the help of (4.2.16). Using Ψ_1, the procedure employed to obtain the initial estimate $\hat{\delta}_0$ is repeated in order to get $\hat{\delta}_1$ defined in a way analogous to $\hat{\delta}_0$. Next, $\hat{\delta}_1$ is utilized to produce another value Ψ_2 of Ψ and so on. The procedure is iterated till tr $(\Psi' W \Psi)$ attains a minimum. We may call this estimator as 'iterative instrumental variables (IIV)' estimator.

Let us now examine the consistency of the estimator given by (4.2.17). Combining the model given in (3.2.3) with (4.2.17) we have the sampling error

$$\hat{\delta} - \delta = (\hat{\overline{Z}}' \hat{W}^{-1} Z)^{-1} \hat{\overline{Z}}' \hat{W}^{-1} w_{**}. \tag{4.2.18}$$

Consider, first, the term

$$\hat{\overline{Z}}' \hat{W}^{-1} w_{**} = \begin{bmatrix} x_{**}' \hat{W}^{-1} w_{**} \\ \hat{\alpha} x_*' \hat{B}' \hat{W}^{-1} w_{**} \end{bmatrix} + \begin{bmatrix} 0 \\ y_1 \hat{a}' \hat{W}^{-1} w_{**} \end{bmatrix}, \tag{4.2.19}$$

because, for a non-stochastic y_1,

$$Ey_* = \alpha Bx_* + y_1 a \quad \text{[cf. equation (3.4.2)]}.$$

In view of the fact that

$$\plim_{T\to\infty} \hat{\alpha} = \alpha, \quad \plim_{T\to\infty} \hat{B} = B \quad \text{and} \quad \plim_{T\to\infty} \hat{W} = W, \tag{4.2.20}$$

and, further, that x_* is uncorrelated with w_{**} (for all t), we get

$$\plim_{T\to\infty} (x'_{**} \hat{W}^{-1} w_{**}/T) = 0 \quad \text{and} \quad \plim_{T\to\infty} (\hat{\alpha} x'_* \hat{B}' \hat{W}^{-1} w_{**}/T) = 0. \tag{4.2.21}$$

The last vector also vanishes in the limit because $Ew_{**} = 0$. Assuming $\plim_{\to\infty} (\hat{\bar{Z}}' \hat{W}^{-1} Z/T)^{-1}$ finite and non-singular, we conclude that $\hat{\delta}$ is consistent.

In order to derive the expression of its asymptotic covariance matrix, consider

$$\plim_{T\to\infty} T(\hat{\delta}-\delta)(\hat{\delta}-\delta)' = \plim_{T\to\infty} T(\hat{\bar{Z}}' \hat{W}^{-1} Z)^{-1} \Big(\plim_{T\to\infty} \frac{1}{T} \hat{\bar{Z}}' \hat{W}^{-1}$$

$$w_{**} w'_{**} \hat{W}^{-1} \hat{\bar{Z}}\Big) \plim_{T\to\infty} T(\hat{\bar{Z}}' \hat{W}^{-1} Z)'^{-1}. \tag{4.2.22}$$

Note that the middle term within parentheses on the right hand side of the equality sign reduces to

$$\plim_{T\to\infty} \frac{1}{T} \bar{Z}' W^{-1} \bar{Z},$$

whereas the value of the first or the last term is $\plim_{T\to\infty} T(\bar{Z}' W^{-1} \bar{Z})^{-1}$. Hence, the asymptotic covariance matrix of the estimator $\hat{\delta}$ derived in (4.2.17) is given by

$$\plim_{T\to\infty} T(\hat{\delta}-\delta)(\hat{\delta}-\delta)' = \plim_{T\to\infty} T(\bar{Z}' W^{-1} \bar{Z})^{-1}. \tag{4.2.23}$$

Comparing it with that of Hannan's estimator, we see that the two are exactly identical.

4.3 ESTIMATION OF THE MODEL – AN EMPIRICAL ANALYSIS

In a recent article Morrison (1970) examined certain small sample properties of alternative methods of estimating the geometric distributed lag model (2.3.4) discussed in Chapter 2. Six methods of estimation were compared through a Monte Carlo experiment involving samples of sizes 20 and 50. In this particular study Dhrymes' search (cf. Section 2.4) turned out to be the best.

Below, we present an illustration comparing numerical magnitudes of different estimates of parameters of the model (2.3.4). The methods of estimation considered are: the least squares, Koyck, Klein, Liviatan and Dhrymes discussed in Chapter 2, and IIV described above. The illustration deals with a consumption function of the distributed lag type;[1]

$$c_t = \alpha_0 + \alpha y_t + \alpha\beta\, y_{t-1} + \alpha\beta^2 y_{t-2} + \ldots + u_t, \tag{4.3.1}$$

where

c_t = real consumption at time t.
y_t = real disposable income at time t.

The relevant time series observations which deal with the U.S. economy (1929-41 and 1946-59) have been taken from Christ (1966, pp. 590-91). Real consumption and real disposable income are measured in billions of 1954 U.S. dollars. The graph of the observed series is shown in Figure 4.1.

It is natural to assume that $0 \leqslant \beta < 1$.[2] We also assume that the mean value of u_t is zero, its variance σ_u^2 (for all t) and $\{u_t\}$ follow a first order Markov process which is specified as Assumption 4 in Chapter 2. Transforming (4.3.1) into the form (2.3.5) we get in matrix notation

$$c_{**} = Z\,\delta + w_{**}, \qquad w_{**} = u_{**} - \beta u_* \tag{4.3.2}$$

where

$$Z = (y_{**} \quad c_* \quad \iota), \qquad \delta = \begin{bmatrix} \alpha \\ \beta \\ \alpha_0\,(1-\beta) \end{bmatrix}$$

and ι is a vector consisting of ones.[3]

First of all, we obtain the least squares and Liviatan's estimates of δ according to the formulae

$$(Z'Z)^{-1}Z'c_{**} \quad \text{and} \quad (\Psi'Z)^{-1}\Psi'c_{**},$$

respectively, where the matrix of instruments Ψ is taken as $\Psi = (y_{**}\ y_*\ \iota)$. The estimates of the residual variance according to both the methods are computed from the formula

67

$$\sigma_w^2 = \sum_1^T w_t^2/T, \quad w_t = c_t - \alpha y_t - \beta c_{t-1} - \alpha_0(1-\beta).$$

The standard errors of the least squares estimates are obtained by using the expression $\sigma_w^2 (Z'Z)^{-1}$. Furthermore, we compute

$$\varrho_w = \sum_2^T w_t w_{t-1} / \sum_2^T w_t^2.$$

An estimate of the first order autocorrelation coefficient, ϱ, between u_t's is determined by applying

$$u_{**} = B^* w_{**} \quad \text{and} \quad \varrho = u'_{**} u_* / u'_{**} u_{**},$$

where B^* is defined in (2.4.74). For estimating the residual variance σ_u^2, the formula

$$\sigma_u^2 = \sum_1^T u_t^2 / T$$

is used. For the asymptotic standard errors of Liviatan's estimates the formula given in (3.3.5) is used, while the expression given in (3.3.1) is employed in order to obtain its finite sample bias. Notice that the expression for Ω in this case is

$$\Omega = Eu_* w'_{**} = \sigma_u^2 \begin{bmatrix} (\varrho-\beta) & \varrho(\varrho-\beta) & \cdots & \varrho^{T-1}(\varrho-\beta) \\ (1-\beta\varrho) & (\varrho-\beta) & & \varrho^{T-2}(\varrho-\beta) \\ \vdots & & & \\ & & & \varrho(\varrho-\beta) \\ \varrho^{T-2}(1-\beta\varrho) & \cdots & (1-\beta\varrho) & (\varrho-\beta) \end{bmatrix}.$$

These results are shown in the first two rows of Table 4.1. Then we iterate in order to obtain the IIV estimator of δ as formulated in the preceding section. For this purpose it is assumed that c_0 is non-stochastic and given. Accordingly,

$$Ec_* = \alpha By_* + c_0 \begin{bmatrix} 1 \\ \beta \\ \vdots \\ \beta^{T-1} \end{bmatrix} + \alpha_0 \begin{bmatrix} 0 \\ 1-\beta \\ \vdots \\ 1-\beta^{T-1} \end{bmatrix},$$

where B is given in (3.2.15). It should be noted that for computing Ec_* the value of y_0 is not required. The results of this procedure can be found in the third row of the table. The asymptotic standard errors are calculated according to the formula (4.2.23).

Koyck's method of estimating (4.3.2) presupposes the knowledge of ϱ. The normal equations without correction for the constant term are given by (2.4.17). Instead of scanning the range of ϱ, as Koyck did, we use a consistent estimate of ϱ from Liviatan's formula and then derive the coefficient estimates. The estimates according to this modified Koyck method (cf. Chapter 2) are presented in the fourth row of the table.

Likewise, Klein's iterative procedure makes use of a starting value of the autocorrelation coefficient ϱ. We may begin the iterations by using either (i) the least squares, or, (ii) Liviatan's consistent estimates of the parameters. Having obtained the coefficient estimates by either of the two methods, we proceed as above and obtain an estimate of ϱ which is used in the initial round of the iterative procedure. Klein's estimates according to (i) and (ii) are given in the fifth row of the table.

Finally, Dhrymes' efficient estimates of the parameters of the model (4.3.1) are found by scanning over the ranges of the parameters β and ϱ such that the residual variance σ^2 is globally minimized. The standard errors of these estimates of α, β and ϱ are obtained by applying, respectively, the formulae given in (2.4.76), (2.4.77) and (2.4.78). Dhrymes' estimates are recorded in the last row of the table.

4.4 CONCLUSIONS

Now some interesting conclusions can be drawn on the basis of our results. Looking at the table we observe that all the parameter estimates are positive in sign. The estimates of the short-run marginal propensity to consume, α, range from 0.617 to 0.720 and those of the long-run marginal propensity to consume, $\alpha/(1-\beta)$, range between 0.918 and 0.905; α is numerically greater than β in all cases. These values are consistent with *a priori* expectations. When presented graphically, different estimates of (α, β) lie approximately on a straight line (see Figure 4.2). Klein's and Dhrymes' estimates occupy extreme positions while other estimates lie between the two. Furthermore, α and β are negatively associated. Although least squares estimates are inconsistent, these compare favourably with those by Liviatan, Modified Koyck and IIV methods. The differences appear to be negligible for practical purposes. This does not surprise us because the estimates of the autocorrelation coefficients, ϱ_w and even ϱ, are positive throughout and are small in magnitude. In terms of standard errors the performance of IIV estimator as compared with that of Liviatan is better but the procedure by Dhrymes has turned out to be the best of all methods considered in the illustration. Regarding Klein's procedure two points are

Table 4.1 Alternative estimates of parameters of the consumption function (4.3.1) and (4.3.2)
Period: 1929-41 and 1946-59

Estimation procedure	Estimates of the parameters			Estimates of the Variance of Disturbances			Estimates of the First Order Autocorrelation Coefficient	
	α	β	$\dfrac{\alpha}{1-\beta}$	σ_w^2	σ_u^2	σ^2	ϱ_w	ϱ
(1)	(2)	(3)	(4)	(5)	(6)	(7)	(8)	(9)
Least Squares	0.66123 (0.05360)	0.27525 (0.06336)	0.912	6.34215	6.83882			0.26754
Liviatan	0.67401 (0.05419) (0.00044)*	0.26001 (0.06385) (–0.00048)*	0.911	6.35574	6.82766		0.07992	0.26095
I I V	0.66209 (0.05059)	0.27418 (0.05955)	0.912	6.34222	6.83639		0.07135	0.26689
Mod. Koyck	0.65966	0.27713	0.913	6.34236				0.26095
Klein (i)	0.61741	0.32751	0.918					0.25170
Klein (ii)	0.61717	0.32777	0.918					0.24597
Dhrymes	0.72040 (0.00745)	0.20426 (0.02251)	0.905			6.90814		0.17672 (0.03717)

The quantities within brackets are the asymptotic standard errors and the brackets marked with an asterisk (*) give bias, correct to order 1/T, according to the formula (3.3.1).

Figure 4.1 Showing real consumption (c_t) and real disposable income (y_t) in billions of 1954 U.S. dollars. Period: 1929-41 and 1946-59

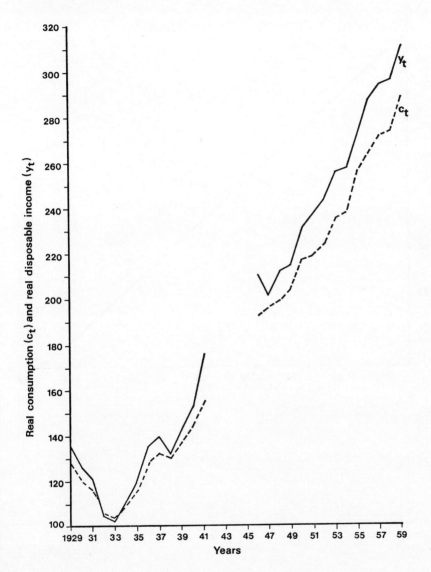

Figure 4.2   Relative positions of alternative estimates

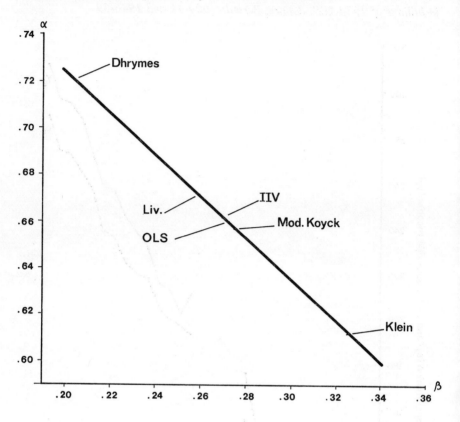

noteworthy; first, the method did not converge irrespective of the precision of the starting value of ϱ, and second, the speed of convergence, though extremely slow, was faster in case the starting value of ϱ was obtained by Liviatan's method than in case it was estimated by least squares, its advantage being in the ratio of about 2:3. Furthermore, the results of the successive iterations were directed towards the β-axis in Figure 4.2. The estimates reported in the table correspond to the 100-th iteration in each case. In terms of computer time IIV performed best among the iterative or scanning methods.

In concluding we should perhaps stress that our analysis is restricted to the asymptotic behaviour of the estimators. A similar analysis based on the small sample properties of these estimators might have led to different conclusions. The latter analysis, which is unfortunately very difficult but realistic, is beyond the scope of the present study.

NOTES

1. Since the model contains a constant term, necessary modifications must be made in the various formulae developed above before they are used in this particular example.
2. A negative value of β will imply an oscillating response to a change in income over time, or symbolically,

$$c_t = \alpha_0 + \alpha y_t - \alpha\beta^* y_{t-1} + \alpha\beta^{*2} y_{t-2} - \ldots + u_t,$$

where $\beta = -\beta^*$ and β^* lies between 0 and 1.
3. For the meaning of vectors marked with one or two asterisks, see footnote 1 in Chapter 3. Further, note that observations on the lagged variable c_* for the years 1928 and 1945 are given whereas those on the lagged variable y_* in these periods are chosen arbitrarily for computing certain statistics.

5. Estimation of simultaneous linear equations

5.1 INTRODUCTION

The discussion in the earlier chapters has remained restricted to the estimation of single equation regression models with lagged variables on the right hand side.

In *interdependent systems* or *simultaneous equations* we face a rather different situation. We have a set of dependent variables (called *endogenous* variables) which are to be explained 'jointly' in terms of *exogenous* or *predetermined* variables. The variables (both endogenous and exogenous) enter symmetrically into each equation – although in practice there is always a natural choice for the left hand dependent variable in each equation.[1] Since the dependent variables are explained jointly or simultaneously (rather than one at a time) the name 'simultaneous equations'.

5.2 THE STRUCTURAL EQUATION SYSTEM

Let us write, under linearity assumptions, M structural equations in $(M + \Lambda)$ observable variables at time t ($t = 1, \ldots, T$) as

$$\gamma_{11}y_1(t) + \ldots + \gamma_{M1}y_M(t) + \beta_{11}x_1(t) + \ldots + \beta_{\Lambda 1}x_\Lambda(t) = u_1(t)$$

$$\ldots \tag{5.2.1}$$

$$\gamma_{1M}y_1(t) + \ldots + \gamma_{MM}y_M(t) + \beta_{1M}x_1(t) + \ldots + \beta_{\Lambda M}x_\Lambda(t) = u_M(t),$$

where γ's and β's are the *structural coefficients* and $u(t)$'s are the *structural disturbances*. Broadly speaking, there are two types of variables entering a structural equation system – exogenous and endogenous. Exogenous variables are those variables which are determined by factors outside the system and are, therefore, treated as fixed and stochastically independent of the random disturbances. Such variables in the above system are represented by x's and these are assumed to be Λ in number. Remaining M

variables, y's, which are 'to be explained' with the help of the equation system are called endogenous variables. The current endogenous variables are called *jointly dependent* variables while lagged variables (both endogenous and exogenous) along with the current exogenous may be termed as *predetermined variables*. In any specific situation whether a particular variable is endogenous or exogenous depends on the underlying economic process. For example, 'fixed capital' may be treated as an exogenous variable in a short-run process but in a long-run model, it may be considered as an endogenous variable.

An equation system in (5.2.1) is said to be *complete* if the number of jointly dependent variables is exactly equal to the number of equations in the system.

5.3 IDENTIFIABILITY CRITERIA IN LINEAR MODELS

It is well known that given a set of simultaneous linear equations, the relationships in the complete system are characterized by certain *a priori* restrictions on its parameters which enable us to determine the structural parameters uniquely. Some of these restrictions are simple zero restrictions specifying particular coefficients to be zero. In other words, not all the variables (jointly dependent and predetermined) of the complete system are necessarily represented in each structural equation. As an illustration, let us consider Tintner's (1954) two-equation model for the American meat market;

Demand equation: $y_1(t) = \gamma_1 y_2(t) + \beta_1 x_1(t) + u_1(t),$ (5.3.1)

Supply equation: $y_1(t) = \gamma_2 y_2(t) + \beta_2 x_2(t) + \beta_3 x_3(t) + u_2(t),$ (5.3.2)

where

$y_1(t) = $ quantity of meat consumed

and

$y_2(t) = $ a (deflated) price index of meat

represent observations on the two jointly dependent variables at time t;

$x_1(t) = $ index of disposable real income

$x_2(t) = $ index of the cost of processing meat

and

$x_3(t) = $ (deflated) index of the cost of producing agricultural products

are observations on the three predetermined variables at time t; $u_1(t)$ and $u_2(t)$ are the structural disturbances and $\gamma_1, \beta_1, \gamma_2, \beta_2$ and β_3 are the structural coefficients to be determined. It may be observed that the variables x_2 and x_3 are excluded from (5.3.1) and x_1 has been excluded from (5.3.2). We may interpret these variables to be entering the respective equations with zero coefficients. Zero restrictions of other types are also not uncommon. For example, coefficients of two variables may be specified to be equal to each other.[2]

We may state the well known identifiability conditions as follows[3];

Order condition of identifiability: 'A necessary condition for the identifiability of a structural equation within a given linear model is that the number of variables excluded from that equation (more generally, the number of linear restrictions on the parameters of that equation) be at least equal to the number of structural equations M, less one.'

Rank condition of identifiability: 'A necessary and sufficient condition for the identifiability of a structural equation within a linear model, restricted only by the exclusion of certain variables from certain equations, is that we can form at least one nonvanishing determinant of order M—1 out of those coefficients, properly arranged, with which the variables excluded from that structural equations appear in the M—1 other structural equations.'

Therefore, one single equation, say i-th of the complete system (5.2.1), may be written as

$$y_i(t) = \sum_{j=1}^{m} \gamma_j y_j(t) + \sum_{j=1}^{l} \beta_j x_j(t) + u_i(t), \qquad (5.3.3)$$

where one of the dependent variables (the choice of which is natural in any practical situation) has been kept on the left hand side, the remaining ones (both endogenous and exogenous) have been transferred to the right, the variables with zero coefficients having been omitted, and the entire equation has been divided through by the coefficient of the left hand dependent variable. Thus, we assume that only $m + 1 \leqslant M$ jointly dependent and $l \leqslant \Lambda$ predetermined variables enter the equation (5.3.3).

An equation of the complete system is said to be *just identified* if we have

$$\Lambda = m + l, \qquad (5.3.4)$$

and *over-identified* if

$$\Lambda > m + l, \qquad (5.3.5)$$

where Λ is the number of predetermined variables occurring in the complete system (5.2.1), l and $m + 1$ are the number of predetermined and jointly dependent variables appearing in the equation under consideration, respectively. The equation is *not identifiable* if $\Lambda < m + l$ and in that case question of estimating its parameters does not arise.

While a number of methods of estimation of the parameters of structural equations in a complete system of simultaneous linear equations are available in the literature, we shall be concerned only with the two-stage least squares estimator and shall examine some of its small sample properties.

5.4 MATRIX FORMULATION OF THE MODEL

Let us first write the structural equation system (5.2.1) in matrix form as

$$YT + XB = U, \tag{5.4.1}$$

where

$$Y = \begin{bmatrix} y_1(1) \; \ldots \; y_M(1) \\ \vdots \\ y_1(T) \qquad y_M(T) \end{bmatrix} \text{ and } X = \begin{bmatrix} x_1(1) \; \ldots \; x_\Lambda(1) \\ \vdots \\ x_1(T) \qquad x_\Lambda(T) \end{bmatrix} \tag{5.4.2}$$

are the $T \times M$ and $T \times \Lambda$ matrices of observations on the jointly dependent and predetermined variables, respectively;

$$\Gamma = \begin{bmatrix} \gamma_{11} \; \cdots \; \gamma_{1M} \\ \vdots \\ \gamma_{M1} \qquad \gamma_{MM} \end{bmatrix} \text{ and } B = \begin{bmatrix} \beta_{11} \; \cdots \; \beta_{1M} \\ \vdots \\ \beta_{\Lambda 1} \qquad \beta_{\Lambda M} \end{bmatrix} \tag{5.4.3}$$

are the $M \times M$ and $\Lambda \times M$ structural coefficient matrices and

$$U = \begin{bmatrix} u_1(1) \; \ldots \; u_M(1) \\ \vdots \\ u_1(T) \qquad u_M(T) \end{bmatrix} \tag{5.4.4}$$

is the $T \times M$ matrix of structural disturbances.

The *reduced form* of the system (5.2.1) is derived by solving the set of structural equations for all the jointly dependent variables in terms of predetermined variables and the structural disturbances. This can easily be done in matrix notation by post multiplying both sides of (5.4.1) by Γ^{-1}, assuming $|\Gamma| \neq 0$. This assumption of non-singularity of the structural coefficient matrix Γ enables one to express each of the current endogenous variables in terms of all the predetermined variables and structural disturbances. Accordingly, we may write

$$Y = X\Pi + \bar{V}, \tag{5.4.5}$$

where

$$\Pi = \begin{bmatrix} \pi_{11} & \cdots & \pi_{1M} \\ \vdots & & \\ \pi_{\Lambda 1} & & \pi_{\Lambda M} \end{bmatrix} = -B\Gamma^{-1} \tag{5.4.6}$$

is the $\Lambda \times M$ matrix of *reduced form coefficients* and

$$\bar{V} = \begin{bmatrix} \bar{v}_1(1) & \cdots & \bar{v}_M(1) \\ \vdots & & \\ \bar{v}_1(T) & & \bar{v}_M(T) \end{bmatrix} = U\Gamma^{-1} \tag{5.4.7}$$

is the $T \times M$ matrix of *reduced form disturbances.*

Writing algebraically, the reduced form equations in (5.4.5) for the t-th period are

$$y_1(t) = \pi_{11}x_1(t) + \ldots + \pi_{\Lambda 1}x_\Lambda(t) + \bar{v}_1(t),$$
$$\vdots \tag{5.4.8}$$
$$y_M(t) = \pi_{1M}x_1(t) + \ldots + \pi_{\Lambda M}x_\Lambda(t) + \bar{v}_M(t), \quad t = 1, \ldots, T.$$

We observe that each equation in the above system contains only one current endogenous variable as a linear function of all the Λ predetermined variables which are supposed to be statistically independent of the reduced form disturbances. Further, the elements of the matrix of reduced form coefficients, Π, in (5.4.6) are functions of the structural parameters occurring in Γ and B. Similarly, it is easy to see that the elements of the reduced form disturbance matrix, $\bar{V}$, are linear functions of the contemporaneous structural disturbances. Thus, postulating the probability distribution of the structural disturbances, one can determine the joint conditional distribution of the jointly dependent variables given observations on all the predetermined variables.

The i-th equation (5.3.3) of the complete equation system may be written in matrix form as follows:

$$y_i = Y_i\gamma_i + X_i\beta_i + u_i = (Y_i \ X_i)\,\delta_i + u_i,$$
$$\delta_i = \begin{pmatrix} \gamma_i \\ \delta_i \end{pmatrix}, \quad i = 1, \ldots, M; \tag{5.4.9}$$

so that y_i is the column vector of T observations on the left hand jointly dependent variable, Y_i and X_i are the $T \times m_i$ and $T \times l_i$ matrices of observations on the right hand jointly dependent and predetermined variables, respectively, in the i-th equation; γ_i and β_i are the coefficient vectors and u_i is the disturbance vector in that equation.

The reduced form corresponding to the right hand jointly dependent variables in (5.4.9) can be written as

$$Y_i = X \Pi_i + \bar{V}_i, \tag{5.4.10}$$

where Π_i and $\bar{V}_i$ are the $\Lambda \times m_i$ and $T \times m_i$ sub-matrices of Π and $\bar{V}$ in (5.4.6) and (5.4.7) respectively.

5.5 ASSUMPTIONS

Let us now lay down the general assumptions underlying the asymptotic theory of the two-stage least squares.

Assumption 1. There are M jointly dependent and Λ predetermined variables connected by a complete set of M linear equations of the form (5.2.1).

Assumption 2. T observations on all the jointly dependent and predetermined variables are given.

Assumption 3. The rank of the matrix X is $\Lambda \leqslant T$. Further, $\Lambda \geqslant m + l$, so that the equation under consideration is identifiable.

Assumption 4. The square matrix Γ in (5.4.1) is non-singular, so that the reduced form of the system exists.

Assumption 5. The T row vectors of the structural disturbances in (5.4.1) are independently and identically distributed such that

(i)   *means:* $E u_i(t) = 0$, *for all t and i*
(ii) *variances:* var $u_i(t) = \sigma_{ii} = \sigma^2$, *for all t*
(iii) *covariances:* cov $[u_i(t), u_j(t')] = \sigma_{ij}, \quad t = t'$
$$= 0, \quad t \neq t'$$

where $i, j = 1, \ldots, M$ and $t, t' = 1, \ldots, T$.

This assumption implies that the structural disturbances are serially independent and have zero means.

Thus, we shall write

$$\Sigma = \begin{bmatrix} \sigma_{11} & \cdots & \sigma_{1M} \\ \vdots & & \\ \sigma_{M1} & & \sigma_{MM} \end{bmatrix} \tag{5.5.1}$$

for the entire matrix of variances and covariances of contemporaneous structural disturbances. Its order is $M \times M$ and is symmetric and positive definite.

5.6 THE TWO-STAGE LEAST SQUARES

The two-stage least squares estimation procedure, which is also known as the 'generalized classical linear (GCL)' method of estimating a single equation of the complete system, was originally proposed by Theil (1961) and it was also independently developed by Basmann (1957).

The first step of the two-stage least squares procedure is to apply classical least squares to (5.4.10) and obtain the estimator

$$\hat{\Pi}_i = (X'X)^{-1} X' Y_i, \tag{5.6.1}$$

and then

$$V_i = Y_i - X(X'X)^{-1} X' Y_i, \tag{5.6.2}$$

is the least squares estimator of $\overline{V}_i$.

The second step consists of replacing Y_i in (5.4.9) by $(Y_i - V_i)$ and then applying least squares to it.

The two-stage least squares estimates of γ_i and β_i are thus given by

$$d_i = \begin{pmatrix} c_i \\ b_i \end{pmatrix} = \left[\begin{pmatrix} Y_i' - V_i' \\ X_i' \end{pmatrix} (Y_i - V_i \, X_i) \right]^{-1} \begin{pmatrix} Y_i' - V_i' \\ X_i' \end{pmatrix} y_i, \tag{5.6.3}$$

where d_i is the two-stage least squares estimator of δ_i as given in (5.4.9).

Using (5.6.2) it is easy to see that $X'V = 0$ implying $X' V_i = 0$ and $Y_i' V_i = V_i' Y_i = V_i' V_i$. Therefore, (5.6.3) reduces to

$$d_i = \begin{pmatrix} c_i \\ b_i \end{pmatrix} = \begin{bmatrix} Y_i' Y_i - V_i' V_i & Y_i' X_i \\ X_i' Y_i & X_i' X_i \end{bmatrix}^{-1} \begin{pmatrix} Y_i' - V_i' \\ X_i' \end{pmatrix} y_i. \tag{5.6.4}$$

It is well known that the two-stage least squares estimates are consistent.

1. For example, in a consumption equation the aggregate consumption is naturally taken to be the left hand dependent variable. Similarly, the investment is the left hand variable in the investment equation.

2. For greater details about the types of zero restriction one might refer to Koopmans, Rubin and Leipnik (1950), pp. 64-65.

3. Cf. Koopmans (1953), p. 38.

6. Properties of the two-stage least squares estimators

6.1 INTRODUCTION

In econometric investigations very often one has to deal with samples of moderate size consisting of time series observations. In a system of simultaneous equations one may estimate the coefficients by the two-stage least squares procedure or by any other method like the three-stage least squares due to Zellner and Theil (1962), the limited or full information maximum likelihood method, respectively, due to Anderson and Rubin (1949) and Koopmans, Rubin and Leipnik (1950). A great deal of attention has been paid towards the asymptotic behaviour of these estimators. So far as the small sample properties of the two-stage least squares (or the general k-class) estimators are concerned, Nagar's (1959a, 1959b) work is well known. Basmann (1957, 1961) worked out exact sampling distributions of the two-stage least squares (GCL) estimators in some special cases. While studying the significance of a linear combination (for example, the sum or difference) of coefficients in different equations one requires the knowledge of variances and covariances of the coefficient estimates. Theil gave the asymptotic covariance matrix of the two-stage least squares estimators of coefficients in two different equations. The asymptotic covariance matrix of the two-stage least squares estimators of coefficients in one single equation can, of course, be treated as a particular case. Further, the three-stage least squares procedure requires *a priori* knowledge of the elements of the covariance matrix, Σ, of structural disturbances according to the two-stage least squares. Suppose $S \equiv ((s_{ij}))$ is the two-stage least squares estimator of $\Sigma \equiv ((\sigma_{ij}))$ such that the diagonal elements s_{ii} are the residual variance estimators of σ_{ii} ($i = 1, \ldots, M$) and the off-diagonal elements s_{ij} are the estimators of the covariances σ_{ij} between contemporaneous disturbances in two different structural equations i and j. It is well known that S is consistent.

The object of the present chapter is twofold. First, we derive the moment matrix, to order $1/T^2$, of the two-stage least squares estimators of coefficients in different equations of the system defined in (5.2.1). The moment matrix, to order $1/T^2$, of the two-stage least squares estimators of coefficients in a single equation derived by Nagar (1959a) will then be a particular case of the result. Second, we analyze the bias, to order $1/T$, of the covariance estimators s_{ij} $(i \neq j)$. The corresponding result for a single equation worked out by Nagar (1961) will also be a particular case of this result.

6.2 THEOREMS ON THE MOMENT MATRIX OF THE TWO-STAGE LEAST SQUARES ESTIMATORS AND BIAS OF THE COVARIANCE MATRIX OF DISTURBANCES

The two-stage least squares procedure of estimating a single equation of the complete system has been discussed in detail in the preceding chapter. Let us consider the estimator given by (5.6.4) where V_i is the $T \times m_i$ matrix of least squares estimated disturbances in that part of the complete reduced form which corresponds to the right hand jointly dependent variables in the i-th structural equation (5.4.9). Since Y_i and X_i are submatrices of Y and X, respectively, we can always write

$$Y A_{1i} = Y_i \quad \text{and} \quad X A_{2i} = X_i, \tag{6.2.1}$$

where the elements of the $M \times m_i$ and $\Lambda \times l_i$ matrices A_{1i} and A_{2i} are necessarily unity and zeros. In any practical situation A_{1i} and A_{2i} will be fully determined. For example, considering Tintner's model described in (5.3.1) and (5.3.2) we observe that there is only one jointly dependent variable occurring on the right hand side of each of the two equations whereas there is one predetermined variable entering (5.3.1) and two in (5.3.2). If we write Tintner's two equations in matrix notation for the t-th period as

$$[y_1(t) \ y_2(t)] \begin{bmatrix} 1 & 1 \\ -\gamma_1 & -\gamma_2 \end{bmatrix} = [x_1(t) \ x_2(t) \ x_3(t)] \begin{bmatrix} \beta_1 & 0 \\ 0 & \beta_2 \\ 0 & \beta_3 \end{bmatrix} +$$

$$+ [u_1(t) \ u_2(t)],$$

then for the first equation $(i = 1)$, A_{1i} is given by the column vector $\begin{pmatrix} 0 \\ 1 \end{pmatrix}$

and A_{2i} by $\begin{pmatrix} 1 \\ 0 \\ 0 \end{pmatrix}$. Similarly, for the second equation $(i = 2)$, A_{1i} is given by

83

$$\begin{pmatrix} 0 \\ 1 \end{pmatrix} \text{ and } A_{2i} \text{ by } \begin{bmatrix} 0 & 0 \\ 1 & 0 \\ 0 & 1 \end{bmatrix}.$$

To analyze the covariance matrix of d_i we introduce the following:
First of all we write

$$Q_i = (C_i'X'XC_i)^{-1} \qquad (6.2.2)$$

and

$$Q_{ij} = (C_i'X'XC_j), \qquad (6.2.3)$$

so that Q_i and Q_{ij} are the parent analogues of

$$\begin{bmatrix} Y_i'Y_i - V_i'V_i & Y_i'X_i \\ X_i'Y_i & X_i'X_i \end{bmatrix}^{-1} \text{ and } \begin{bmatrix} Y_i'Y_j - V_i'V_j & Y_i'X_j \\ X_i'Y_j & X_i'X_j \end{bmatrix}$$

respectively, where

$$C_i = (-B\Gamma^{-1}A_{1i} \quad A_{2i}) \qquad (6.2.4)$$

is a $\Lambda \times n_i$ matrix; $n_i = m_i + l_i$ being the total number of coefficients to be estimated in the i-th equation (5.4.9). Further, the $m_i \times m_j$ covariance matrix of the reduced form disturbances in $\overline{V}_i$ and $\overline{V}_j$ [see equation (5.4.10)] is

$$\Omega_{ij}^* = (1/T) E (\overline{V}_i'\overline{V}_j) \qquad (6.2.5)$$

and bordering this matrix by l_i rows and l_j columns of zeros we get the $n_i \times n_j$ matrix

$$\Omega_{ij} = \begin{bmatrix} \Omega_{ij}^* & 0 \\ 0 & 0 \end{bmatrix} = D_i' \Sigma D_j, \qquad (6.2.6)$$

where

$$D_i = (\Gamma^{-1}A_{1i} \quad 0) \qquad (6.2.7)$$

is an $M \times n_i$ matrix. Lastly, we define

84

$$q_{ij} = \begin{bmatrix} \dfrac{1}{T} E\, Y_i' u_j \\[2mm] \dfrac{1}{T} E\, X_i' u_j \end{bmatrix} = \begin{bmatrix} \dfrac{1}{T} E\, \overline{V}_i' u_j \\[2mm] \underline{0} \end{bmatrix} = D_i'\, \sigma_j, \qquad (6.2.8)$$

which is an $n_i \times 1$ column vector of covariances between the right hand variables (both jointly dependent and predetermined) in the i-th structural equation and the structural disturbance of the j-th equation and

$$\sigma_i = \begin{bmatrix} \sigma_{1i} \\ \vdots \\ \sigma_{Mi} \end{bmatrix}, \qquad (6.2.9)$$

denotes the i-th column of the Σ-matrix defined in (5.5.1).

It is easy to write down similar expressions for other symbols like Q_j, Q_{ji}, C_j, Ω_{jj}, D_j, q_{ji}, σ_j etc., by interchanging the suffixes i and j in the expressions of the corresponding symbols given above.

Assumption 6. The elements of the $T \times \Lambda$ matrix X of observations on all the predetermined variables in (5.4.1) and (5.4.2) are non-stochastic and fixed in repeated samples.

It should be noted that this assumption does not permit the presence of lagged endogenous variables in X. However, in most cases, specially in large sample analysis, the independence of predetermined variables and the structural disturbances is all that is required. For example, the two-stage least squares, limited information maximum likelihood and three-stage least squares estimators do not loose the property of 'consistency' even if lagged endogenous variables are present.

Assumption 7. In addition to the Assumption 5 stated in the preceding chapter, the T row vectors of structural disturbances are assumed to be normally distributed according to an M dimensional normal law.

Then we can state the following theorem:

Theorem I. Under the Assumptions 1 through 5, given in Section 5.5 and the Assumptions 6 and 7 stated above, the moment matrix, to order $1/T^2$, of the two-stage least squares estimates of coefficients in the i-th and the *j-th equations of the complete system* (5.2.1) *about their true parameter values is given by*

$$E(d_i - \delta_i)(d_j - \delta_j)' = \mathscr{V} + V, \tag{6.2.10}$$

where

$$\mathscr{V} = \sigma_{ij} Q_i Q_{ij} Q_j, \tag{6.2.11}$$

and

$$V = a\lambda_1 \mathscr{V} + \lambda_2 Q_i W_1 Q_j + \lambda_1^2 \mathscr{V} q_{ji} q_{ij}' \mathscr{V} +$$
$$+ \lambda_3 \lambda_4 Q_i q_{ii} q_j' Q_j + \lambda_1 (\lambda_3 Q_i W_2 \mathscr{V} + \lambda_4 \mathscr{V} W_3 Q_j) -$$
$$- \lambda_1 (\mathscr{V} Q_{ij}' Q_i W_1 Q_j + Q_i W_1 Q_j Q_{ij}' \mathscr{V}), \tag{6.2.12}$$

$$W_1 = q_{ij} q_{ji}' + \sigma_{ij} \Omega_{ij},$$
$$W_2 = q_{ij} q_{ii}' + \sigma_{ij} \Omega_{ii}, \tag{6.2.13}$$
$$W_3 = q_{jj} q_{ji}' + \sigma_{ij} \Omega_{jj},$$

$$a = \lambda_3 \operatorname{tr}(Q_i q_{ii} q_{ij}') + \lambda_4 \operatorname{tr}(Q_j q_{jj} q_{ji}') - \operatorname{tr}(\Omega_{ij}' \mathscr{V}), \tag{6.2.14}$$

$$\lambda_1 = -1/\sigma_{ij}, \qquad \lambda_2 = (\lambda_3 + \lambda_4 - \Lambda) - \lambda_1 \operatorname{tr}(\mathscr{V} Q_{ij}'),$$
$$\lambda_3 = \Lambda - n_i - 1, \qquad \lambda_4 = \Lambda - n_j - 1. \tag{6.2.15}$$

Corollary 1. Under the assumptions of the above theorem, the asymptotic covariance matrix of the two-stage least squares estimates of coefficients in the i-th and j-th equations of the complete system (5.2.1) *is given by*

$$\operatorname*{plim}_{T \to \infty} T(d_i - \delta_i)(d_j - \delta_j)' = \sigma_{ij} \operatorname*{plim}_{T \to \infty} TQ_i Q_{ij} Q_j. \tag{6.2.16}$$

Corollary 2. Under the same assumptions as above the moment matrix, to order $1/T^2$, of the two-stage least squares estimates of coefficients in one single equation (say the i-th) of the complete system can be written as

$$E(d - \delta)(d - \delta)' = \sigma^2 Q(I + A^*), \tag{6.2.17}$$

where

$$A^* = \{-(2L-3) \operatorname{tr}(C_1 Q) + \operatorname{tr}(C_2 Q)\}. I +$$
$$+ \{(L-2)^2 + 2\} C_1 Q - (L-2) C_2 Q, \tag{6.2.18}$$

86

the suffix i having been dropped throughout and

$$\Omega = C_1 + C_2, \quad C_1 = qq'/\sigma^2, \quad L = \Lambda - (m + l), \tag{6.2.19}$$

σ^2 *being the residual variance of the equation under consideration.*

Residual covariance estimation

The residual variance σ_{ii} of the i-th equation (5.4.9) of the complete system can be estimated by

$$s_{ii} = \frac{1}{T} \hat{u}_i' \hat{u}_i, \tag{6.2.20}$$

where

$$\hat{u}_i = y_i - Z_i d_i = u_i - Z_i e_i; \quad i = 1, \ldots, M. \tag{6.2.21}$$

e_i is the sampling error of d_i and $Z_i = (Y_i \ X_i)$.

The off-diagonal elements of the Σ matrix can be estimated in the same way. For example, the estimator of σ_{ij} is

$$s_{ij} = \frac{1}{T} \hat{u}_i' \hat{u}_j. \tag{6.2.22}$$

Thus, the elements of

$$S = \begin{bmatrix} s_{11} & \cdots & s_{1M} \\ \vdots & & \\ s_{M1} & & s_{MM} \end{bmatrix} \tag{6.2.23}$$

are the estimators of the corresponding elements of the Σ matrix defined in (5.5.1).

We may now state the following theorem:

Theorem II. Under the Assumptions 1 to 7 given in Sections 5.5 and 6.2 we have

$$Es_{ij} - \sigma_{ij} = \sigma_{ij} \left[\frac{1}{T} \{ -n_i - n_j + \text{tr}(Q_i \overline{Z}_i' Z_j Q_j \overline{Z}_j' Z_i) \} + \right.$$

$$+ \{ -(\Lambda - n_i - 1) \, \text{tr}(Q_i W_1) - (\Lambda - n_j - 1) \, \text{tr}(Q_j W_2) +$$

$$\left. + \text{tr}(Q_j \overline{Z}_j' Z_i Q_i \Omega_{ij}) \} \right], \tag{6.2.24}$$

with $W_1 = \dfrac{1}{\sigma_{ij}} q_{ij} q_{ii}'$ *and* $W_2 = \dfrac{1}{\sigma_{ij}} q_{jj} q_{ji}'$, $\overline{Z}_i = EZ_i = XC_i$, Q_i, Q_j, Ω_{ij}, C_i *etc. are all defined above and terms of higher order of smallness than* $1/T$ *have been neglected.*

87

Corollary: Under the same assumptions as of the theorem, the bias to order $1/T$ of the residual variance estimator s_{ii} is

$$Es_{ii} - \sigma_{ii} = \sigma_{ii}\{-\frac{1}{T}n_i - 2(\Lambda - n_i - 1)\operatorname{tr}(Q_i W) + \operatorname{tr}(Q_i \Omega_{ii})\}, (6.2.25)$$

where $W_1 = W_2 = W$ when $i = j$.[1]

6.3 PROOF OF THEOREM I

If we combine (5.4.9) and (5.6.4) we obtain the sampling error of the two-stage least squares estimator d_i of the parameter vector δ_i in the i-th equation (5.4.9) as

$$e_i = d_i - \delta_i = \begin{bmatrix} Y_i'M^*Y_i & Y_i'X_i \\ X_i'Y_i & X_i'X_i \end{bmatrix}^{-1} \begin{bmatrix} Y_i'M^*u_i \\ X_i'u_i \end{bmatrix}, \qquad (6.3.1)$$

where

$$M^* = X(X'X)^{-1}X'. \qquad (6.3.2)$$

As indicated in (6.2.1) let us replace Y_i by YA_{1i} and X_i by XA_{2i} in (6.3.1). Further, with the aid of the equations (5.4.5)-(5.4.7), which give the reduced form

$$Y = -XB\Gamma^{-1} + U\Gamma^{-1}, \qquad (6.3.3)$$

of the complete system, we get

$$e_i = (C_i'X'XC_i + C_i'X'UD_i + D_i'U'XC_i + D_i'U'M^*UD_i)^{-1} \times$$
$$\times (C_i'X'u_i + D_i'U'M^*u_i), \qquad (6.3.4)$$

or, alternatively,

$$e_i = (I + Q_i\Delta_i)^{-1} Q_i (C_i'X'u_i + D_i'U'M^*u_i), \qquad (6.3.5)$$

where

$$\Delta_i = C_i'X'UD_i + D_i'U'XC_i + D_i'U'M^*UD_i, \qquad (6.3.6)$$

and Q_i has been defined in (6.2.2). Thus, Q_i is in fact the probability limit of the $n_i \times n_i$ matrix on the right hand side of (6.3.1).

It can be verified that all the elements of Q_i are of order $1/T$ in probability and considering the elements of Δ_i we observe that

$$\Delta_i = \Delta_{i1/2} + \Delta_{i0}, \tag{6.3.7}$$

where[2]

$$\Delta_{i1/2} = C_i'X'UD_i + D_i'U'XC_i \tag{6.3.8}$$

is of order $\sqrt{T}$, and

$$\Delta_{i0} = D_i'U'M^*UD_i \tag{6.3.9}$$

is of order T^0 or 1 in probability. Thus the suffixes $1/2$ and 0 in $\Delta_{i1/2}$ and Δ_{i0} indicate their orders of magnitude in probability. Further, we note that

$$\operatorname*{plim}_{T\to\infty} \frac{1}{\sqrt{T}} C_i'X' u_i = \operatorname*{plim}_{T\to\infty} \frac{1}{\sqrt{T}} \begin{bmatrix} Y_i'M^*u_i \\ X_i'u_i \end{bmatrix} \tag{6.3.10}$$

is an $n_i \times 1$ column vector whose elements are of order $\sqrt{T}$ and $D_i'U'M^*u_i$ is of order 'unity' in probability.

The sampling error e_j of the two-stage least squares estimator d_j of the parameter vector δ_j in the j-th equation of the system can be written down immediately by replacing i by j in (6.3.5). Then we can write

$$e_ie_j' = (I + Q_i\Delta_i)^{-1} Q_iPQ_j (I + Q_j\Delta_j)'^{-1}; \tag{6.3.11}$$

or, on expanding the right hand side and pre and post multiplying both sides by Q_i^{-1} and Q_j^{-1}, respectively, we get[3]

$$Q_i^{-1} e_ie_j'Q_j^{-1} = P - (PQ_j\Delta_j + \Delta_iQ_iP) + (PQ_j\Delta_jQ_j\Delta_j +$$
$$+ \Delta_iQ_iPQ_j\Delta_j + \Delta_iQ_i\Delta_iQ_iP) - \ldots, \tag{6.3.12}$$

where the symbols with suffix j are similar to the corresponding ones with suffix i, and

$$P = P_1 + P_{1/2} + P_0, \tag{6.3.13}$$

such that

$$\begin{aligned}
P_1 &= C_i'X'u_iu_j'XC_j \\
P_{1/2} &= C_i'X'u_iu_j'M^*UD_j + D_i'U'M^*u_iu_j'XC_j \\
P_0 &= D_i'U'M^*u_iu_j'M^*UD_j,
\end{aligned} \tag{6.3.14}$$

are matrices of orders T, $T^{1/2}$ and one respectively.

It should be noted that to evaluate the mathematical expectation of e_ie_j', to order $1/T^2$, we may retain terms to order 1 only on the right hand side of (6.3.12) because on the left hand side e_ie_j' has already been pre and post multiplied by Q_i^{-1} and Q_j^{-1}, which are both of order T in probability.

Now we observe that

$$EP = EP_1 + EP_{1/2} + EP_0, \tag{6.3.15}$$

where

$$EP_1 = E(C_i'X'u_iu_j'XC_j) = \sigma_{ij}C_i'X'XC_j = \sigma_{ij}Q_{ij}, \tag{6.3.16}$$

Q_{ij} is defined in (6.2.3) and

$$EP_{1/2} = \underline{0}, \tag{6.3.17}$$

$\underline{0}$ being an $n_i \times n_j$ null matrix, because the structural disturbances are assumed to follow an M-dimensional normal law and they are temporally independent. Further, we have

$$EP_0 = D_i' E(U'M^*u_iu_j'M^*U) D_j, \tag{6.3.18}$$

and using (B.5) of the appendix,

$$EP_0 = D_i' (\Lambda^2\sigma_i\sigma_j' + \Lambda\sigma_j\sigma_i' + \Lambda\sigma_{ij} \Sigma) D_j, \tag{6.3.19}$$

σ_i and σ_j being the i-th and the j-th columns of the $M \times M$ matrix, $\Sigma \equiv ((\sigma_{ij}))$.

Therefore,

$$EP = \sigma_{ij}Q_{ij} + \Lambda D_i' (\Lambda\sigma_i\sigma_j' + \sigma_j\sigma_i' + \sigma_{ij} \Sigma) D_j. \tag{6.3.20}$$

Next we consider the mathematical expectation of

$$PQ_j\Delta_j = P_1Q_j\Delta_{j1/2} + (P_1Q_j\Delta_{j0} + P_{1/2}Q_j\Delta_{j1/2}), \tag{6.3.21}$$

where the terms of higher order of smallness than 1 have been omitted from the right hand side. Using (6.3.8) and (6.3.14), we find that

$$E(P_1Q_j\Delta_{j1/2}) = C_i'X' E(u_iu_j'F_jU) D_j +$$
$$+ C_i'X' E(u_iu_j'G_jU') X C_j = \underline{0}, \tag{6.3.22}$$

where 0 is an $n_i \times n_j$ null matrix,

$$F_j = XC_jQ_jC_j'X' \tag{6.3.23}$$

and

$$G_j = XC_jQ_jD_j'. \tag{6.3.24}$$

The mathematical expectation of the second term on the right hand side of (6.3.21) can easily be evaluated by using (B.13) of the appendix as

90

$$E(P_1 Q_j \Lambda_{j0}) = Q_{ij} Q_j D_j' (\sigma_i \sigma_j' + \sigma_j \sigma_i' + \Lambda \sigma_{ij} \Sigma) D_j. \tag{6.3.25}$$

The mathematical expectation of the third term on the right hand side of (6.3.21) can be written as

$$\begin{aligned}
E(P_{1/2} Q_j \Lambda_{j1/2}) =\ & C_i' X' \, E(u_i u_j' M^* U G_j' U) D_j + \\
&+ C_i' X' \, E(u_i u_j' M^* U H_j U') \, X \, C_j + \\
&+ D_i' \, E(U' \, M^* u_i u_j' F_j U) \, D_j + \\
&+ D_i' \, E(U' \, M^* u_i u_j' G_j U') \, X \, C_j, \tag{6.3.26}
\end{aligned}$$

and with the aid of (B.1), (B.7), (B.17) and (B.21) we get

$$\begin{aligned}
E(P_{1/2} Q_j \Lambda_{j1/2}) =\ & Q_{ij} Q_j D_j' (\sigma_i \sigma_j' + \Lambda \sigma_j \sigma_i' + \sigma_{ij} \Sigma) \, D_j + \\
&+ Q_{ij} \{(\Lambda + 1)(\sigma_i' H_j \, \sigma_j) + \sigma_{ij} \, \mathrm{tr}(H_j \, \Sigma)\} + \\
&+ n_j D_i' (\Lambda \, \sigma_i \sigma_j' + \sigma_j \sigma_i' + \sigma_{ij} \Sigma) \, D_j + \\
&+ D_i' (\Lambda \, \sigma_i \sigma_j' + \sigma_j \sigma_i' + \sigma_{ij} \Sigma) \, D_j, \tag{6.3.27}
\end{aligned}$$

where

$$H_j = D_j Q_j D_j'. \tag{6.3.28}$$

Now combining (6.3.21), (6.3.22), (6.3.25) and (6.3.27) and using (6.2.6) and (6.2.8) we obtain

$$\begin{aligned}
E(P Q_j \Lambda_j) =\ & Q_{ij} Q_j \{2 q_{ji} q_{jj}' + (\Lambda + 1) \, W_3\} + \\
&+ \Lambda \, (n_j + 1) \, q_{ii} q_{jj}' + (n_j + 1) \, W_1 + \\
&+ \{(\Lambda + 1) \, \mathrm{tr}(H_j \sigma_j \sigma_i') + \sigma_{ij} \, \mathrm{tr}(H_j \, \Sigma)\} \, Q_{ij}. \tag{6.3.29}
\end{aligned}$$

The mathematical expectation of the third term on the right hand side of (6.3.12), viz., $E(\Lambda_i Q_i P)$, can be obtained from (6.3.29) by taking its transpose and interchanging the suffixes i and j;

$$\begin{aligned}
E(\Lambda_i Q_i P) =\ & \{2 q_{ii} q_{ij}' + (\Lambda + 1) \, W_2\} \, Q_i Q_{ij} + \\
&+ \Lambda \, (n_i + 1) \, q_{ii} q_{jj}' + (n_i + 1) \, W_1 + \\
&+ \{(\Lambda + 1) \, \mathrm{tr}(H_i \, \sigma_i \sigma_j') + \sigma_{ij} \, \mathrm{tr}(H_i \, \Sigma)\} \, Q_{ij}. \tag{6.3.30}
\end{aligned}$$

Let us consider the fourth term on the right hand side of (6.3.12), viz.,

$$\begin{aligned}
P Q_j \Lambda_j Q_j \Lambda_j =\ & P_1 Q_j \Lambda_{j1/2} Q_j \Lambda_{j1/2} \\
=\ & C_i' X' u_i u_j' F_j U G_j' U D_j + C_i' X' u_i u_j' F_j U H_j U' X C_j + \\
&+ C_i' X' u_i u_j' G_j U' F_j U D_j + C_i' X' u_i u_j' G_j U' G_j U' X C_j, \tag{6.3.31}
\end{aligned}$$

where the terms of higher order of smallness than one have been omitted and F_j, G_j and H_j have been introduced in (6.3.23), (6.3.24) and (6.3.28). Therefore, we have

$$
\begin{aligned}
E(PQ_j\Delta_jQ_j\Delta_j) =\ & Q_{ij}Q_jD_j'\,(\sigma_i\sigma_j' + n_j\sigma_j\sigma_i' + \sigma_{ij}\,\Sigma)\,D_j + \\
& + \{(n_j + 1)\,(\sigma_i'H_j\sigma_j) + \sigma_{ij}\,\mathrm{tr}(H_j\,\Sigma)\}\,Q_{ij} + \\
& + Q_{ij}Q_jD_j'\,(\sigma_i\sigma_j' + \sigma_j\sigma_i' + n_j\sigma_{ij}\,\Sigma)\,D_j + \\
& + Q_{ij}\{(\sigma_i'H_j\sigma_j)\,I + Q_jD_j'\sigma_j\sigma_i'D_j + \\
& + \sigma_{ij}Q_jD_j'\,\Sigma\,D_j\},
\end{aligned}
\tag{6.3.32}
$$

the relevant expectations having been obtained in (B.20), (B.25), (B.16) and (B.26). Using (6.2.6) and (6.2.8), this simplifies to

$$
\begin{aligned}
E(PQ_j\Delta_jQ_j\Delta_j) =\ & Q_{ij}Q_j\,\{2q_{ji}q_{jj}' + (n_j + 2)\,W_3\} + \\
& + \{(n_j + 2)\,\mathrm{tr}(H_j\sigma_j\sigma_i') + \sigma_{ij}\,\mathrm{tr}(H_j\,\Sigma)\}\,Q_{ij}.
\end{aligned}
\tag{6.3.33}
$$

Now we consider the fifth term on the right hand side of (6.3.12), viz.,

$$
\begin{aligned}
\Delta_iQ_iPQ_j\Delta_j =\ & \Delta_{i1/2}Q_iP_1Q_j\Delta_{j1/2} \\
=\ & C_i'X'UG_i'u_iu_j'F_jUD_j + C_i'X'UG_i'u_iu_j'G_jU'XC_j + \\
& + D_i'U'F_iu_iu_j'F_jUD_j + D_i'U'F_iu_iu_j'G_jU'XC_j,
\end{aligned}
\tag{6.3.34}
$$

up to order 1 only. Taking expectations on both sides of (6.3.34) and using (B.12), (B.30), (B.6) and (B.11) we get

$$
E(\Delta_iQ_iPQ_j\Delta_j)
\tag{6.3.35}
$$

$$
\begin{aligned}
=\ & (n_jD_i'\sigma_i\sigma_j' + Q_{ij}Q_jQ_{ij}'Q_iD_i'\sigma_j\sigma_i' + \sigma_{ij}Q_{ij}Q_jQ_{ij}'Q_iD_i'\,\Sigma)\,D_j + \\
& + \{D_i'\sigma_i\sigma_j'D_j + Q_{ij}Q_jD_j'\sigma_i\sigma_j'D_iQ_iQ_{ij} + \sigma_{ij}\,\mathrm{tr}(G_i\,\Sigma\,G_j')\,Q_{ij}\} + \\
& + D_i'\,\{n_in_j\sigma_i\sigma_j' + (\sigma_j\sigma_i' + \sigma_{ij}\Sigma)\,\mathrm{tr}(Q_iQ_{ij}Q_jQ_{ij}')\}\,D_j + \\
& + D_i'\,(n_i\sigma_i\sigma_j'D_j + \sigma_j\sigma_i'D_jQ_jQ_{ij}'Q_iQ_{ij} + \sigma_{ij}\Sigma D_jQ_jQ_{ij}'Q_iQ_{ij}),
\end{aligned}
$$

or, more compactly,

$$
E(\Delta_iQ_iPQ_j\Delta_j)
$$

$$
\begin{aligned}
=\ & (n_i + n_j + n_in_j + 1)\,q_{ii}q_{jj}' + W_1\,\mathrm{tr}(Q_iQ_{ij}Q_jQ_{ij}') + \\
& + (Q_{ij}Q_jQ_{ij}'Q_iW_1 + W_1Q_jQ_{ij}'Q_iQ_{ij}) + \\
& + \sigma_{ij}Q_{ij}\,\mathrm{tr}(G_i\,\Sigma\,G_j') + Q_{ij}Q_jq_{ji}q_{ij}'Q_iQ_{ij}.
\end{aligned}
\tag{6.3.36}
$$

Finally, the mathematical expectation of the last term on the right hand side of (6.3.12), viz. $E(\Delta_i Q_i \Delta_i Q_i P)$, is directly obtained from (6.3.33) by taking its transpose and interchanging the suffixes i and j;

$$E(\Delta_i Q_i \Delta_i Q_i P) = \{2q_{ii}q'_{ij} + (n_i + 2)W_2\} Q_i Q_{ij} +$$

$$+ \{(n_i + 2)\,\mathrm{tr}(H_i \sigma_j \sigma'_i) + \sigma_{ij}\,\mathrm{tr}(H_i \, \Sigma)\} Q_{ij}. \qquad (6.3.37)$$

Hence, combining (6.3.12), (6.3.20), (6.3.29), (6.3.30), (6.3.33), (6.3.36) and (6.3.37) and rearranging the terms therein with the help of (6.2.6), (6.2.8), (6.3.23), (6.3.24) and (6.3.28), the result stated in Theorem I follows.

6.4 PROOF OF THEOREM II

We have to obtain the mathematical expectation of

$$s_{ij} - \sigma_{ij} = \frac{1}{T}\hat{u}'_i\hat{u}_j - \sigma_{ij}, \qquad (6.4.1)$$

to order $1/T$ in probability. Therefore, according to (6.2.21) if we write

$$\hat{u}'_i\hat{u}_j = (u_i - Z_i e_i)' (u_j - Z_j e_j)$$

$$= u'_i u_j - u'_i Z_j e_j - e'_i Z'_i u_j + e'_i Z'_i Z_j e_j, \qquad (6.4.2)$$

and derive mathematical expectation of individual terms on its right hand side we need retain terms only to order 1 in probability, because later they have to be multiplied by $1/T$.

Considering the first term we get[4]

$$Eu'_i u_j = \sum_t E\{u_i(t)u_j(t)\} = T\sigma_{ij}, \qquad (6.4.3)$$

due to Assumption 5 given in Section 5.5.

Next we evaluate the expectation of the second term in (6.4.2).

$$E(u'_i Z_j e_j) = E\{u'_i\,(\bar{Z}_j + UD_j)e_j\} = E(u'_i F_j u_j) +$$

$$+ E(u'_i UH_j U'M^* u_j) - E(u'_i UG'_j UG'_j u_j) -$$

$$- E(u'_i UH_j U'F_j u_j), \qquad (6.4.4)$$

where F_j, G_j, H_j are respectively $T \times T$, $T \times M$, $M \times M$ matrices consisting of non-stochastic elements and are defined in (6.3.23), (6.3.24) and (6.3.28); e_j, up to order $1/T$, has been obtained from (6.3.5) by replacing

93

the suffix i by j therein, and use has been made of the fact that all odd order moments of a multivariate normal distribution are zero.

Considering the first term on the right hand side of the second equality of (6.4.4), we get

$$E(u_i' F_j u_j) = \text{tr}\,\{F_j E(u_j u_i')\} = \sigma_{ij}\,\text{tr}F_j = \sigma_{ij} n_j, \qquad (6.4.5)$$

because

$$\text{tr}F_j = \text{tr}(\bar{Z}_j Q_j \bar{Z}_j') = \text{tr}\{(\bar{Z}_j'\bar{Z}_j)\,(\bar{Z}_j'\bar{Z}_j)^{-1}\} = \text{tr}I = n_j, \qquad (6.4.6)$$

I being an $n_j \times n_j$ unit matrix.

The second term on the right hand side of the second equality of (6.4.4) is written as

$$E(u_i' U H_j U' M^* u_j)$$
$$= \sum_\mu \sum_{\mu'} \sum_t \sum_{t'} \sum_{t''} h_j(\mu, \mu') m^*(t', t'')\, E\{u_i(t)u_\mu(t)u_{\mu'}(t')u_j(t'')\} \qquad (6.4.7)$$

where $h_j(\mu, \mu')$ and $m^*(t', t'')$ are the (μ, μ')-th and (t', t'')-th elements of the $M \times M$ and $T \times T$ matrices H_j and M^*, respectively, defined in (6.3.28) and (6.3.2).

The individual terms on the right hand side of (6.4.7) be non zero only if, either (a) $t = t' = t''$ or (b) $t' = t''$ but $t \neq t'$.

In case (a) we have

$$\{\sum_t m^*(t, t)\}\,\{\sum_\mu \sum_{\mu'} h_j(\mu, \mu')\,(\sigma_{ij}\sigma_{\mu\mu'} + \sigma_{i\mu}\sigma_{j\mu'} + \sigma_{i\mu'}\,\sigma_{j\mu})\}, \qquad (6.4.8)$$

and in case (b)

$$(T - 1)\,\{\sum_t m^*(t, t)\}\,\{\sum_\mu \sum_{\mu'} h_j(\mu, \mu')\,\sigma_{i\mu}\sigma_{j\mu'}\}. \qquad (6.4.9)$$

Therefore, adding (6.4.8) and (6.4.9) and retaining terms to order 1 in probability we get

$$E(u_i' U H_j U' M^* u_j) = T\Lambda \sum_\mu \sum_{\mu'} h_j(\mu, \mu')\sigma_{i\mu}\sigma_{j\mu'} = T\Lambda\sigma_i'H_j\sigma_j$$
$$= T\Lambda\sigma_i'D_j Q_j D_j'\sigma_j = T\Lambda q_{ji}'Q_j q_{jj}, \qquad (6.4.10)$$

where the elements of H_j are of order $1/T$, σ_i and σ_j are the i-th and j-th columns of the Σ matrix and use has been made of (6.2.8) by arranging the suffixes properly.

Similarly, the value of the third term on the right hand side of the second equality in (6.4.4) is easy to obtain as

$$E(u_i' U G_j' U G_j u_j) = T\,\sigma_i'G_j'G_j\sigma_j = T\,\sigma_i'H_j\sigma_j = T\,q_{ji}'Q_j q_{jj}, \qquad (6.4.11)$$

94

to order 1, because $G_j'G_j = H_j$, and we have seen in (6.4.10) that $\sigma_i'H_j\sigma_j = q_{ji}'Q_jq_{jj}$.

The fourth term on the right hand side of the second equality of (6.4.4) can be evaluated from (6.4.10) by replacing M^* by F_j;

$$E(u_i'UH_jU'F_ju_j) = Tn_jq_{ji}'Q_jq_{jj}. \tag{6.4.12}$$

Combining (6.4.4), (6.4.5), (6.4.10), (6.4.11) and (6.4.12) we get the expected value of the second term in (6.4.2) as

$$E(u_i'Z_je_j) = n_j\sigma_{ij} + T(\Lambda - n_j - 1)q_{ji}'Q_jq_{jj}. \tag{6.4.13}$$

The expectation of the third term on the right hand side of the expression (6.4.2) can be obtained directly from (6.4.13) by taking its transpose and interchanging the suffixes i and j. Thus, we have

$$E(e_i'Z_i'u_j) = n_i\sigma_{ij} + T(\Lambda - n_i - 1)q_{ii}'Q_iq_{ij}. \tag{6.4.14}$$

Finally, we consider the expectation of the last term on the right hand side of (6.4.2) and write

$$E(e_i'Z_i'Z_je_j) = E\{e_i'\,(\overline{Z}_i + UD_i)'\,(\overline{Z}_j + UD_j)e_j\}.$$

This may also be written as

$$E(e_i'Z_i'Z_je_j) = E(u_i'F_iF_ju_j) + E(u_i'G_iU'UG_j'u_j), \tag{6.4.15}$$

where e_i and e_j, to order $1/T$, have been obtained from (6.3.5).

Now it is easy to verify that

$$E(u_i'F_iF_ju_j) = \sigma_{ij}\,\mathrm{tr}(F_iF_j) = \sigma_{ij}\,\mathrm{tr}(Q_i\overline{Z}_i'\overline{Z}_jQ_j\overline{Z}_j'\overline{Z}_i), \tag{6.4.16}$$

and the value of the second term on the right of (6.4.15) as

$$E(u_i'G_iU'UG_j'u_j) = T\sigma_{ij}\,\mathrm{tr}\,(\Sigma\,G_j'G_i)$$

$$= T\sigma_{ij}\,\mathrm{tr}\,(\Sigma\,D_jQ_j\overline{Z}_j'\overline{Z}_iQ_iD_i')$$

$$= T\sigma_{ij}\,\mathrm{tr}\,(Q_j\overline{Z}_j'\overline{Z}_iQ_i\Omega_{ij}). \tag{6.4.17}$$

Therefore, combining (6.4.15), (6.4.16) and (6.4.17) we get

$$E(e_i'Z_i'Z_je_j) = \sigma_{ij}\,\mathrm{tr}(Q_i\overline{Z}_i'\overline{Z}_jQ_j\overline{Z}_j'\overline{Z}_i) +$$

$$+ T\sigma_{ij}\,\mathrm{tr}(Q_j\overline{Z}_j'\overline{Z}_iQ_i\Omega_{ij}). \tag{6.4.18}$$

Finally substituting (6.4.3), (6.4.13), (6.4.14) and (6.4.18) into (6.4.2) we get the result stated in Theorem II.

APPENDIX A. MOMENTS OF AN M-DIMENSIONAL NORMAL DISTRIBUTION[5]

The structural disturbances $u_1(t), \ldots, u_M(t)$ – for any $t = 1, \ldots, T$ – of the complete equation system (5.2.1) have been assumed to follow an M-dimensional normal law with means zero and a covariance matrix $\Sigma \equiv ((\sigma_{ij}))$, σ_{ij} being the covariance between the contemporaneous disturbances of the i-th and the j-th equations $(i, j = 1, \ldots, M)$:

$$\frac{|\Sigma|^{-1/2}}{(2\pi)^{M/2}} \exp\left(-\tfrac{1}{2} u'_t \Sigma^{-1} u_t\right) du_1(t) \ldots du_M(t), \tag{A.1}$$

where $|\Sigma|$ is the determinant value of Σ and

$$u'_t = [u_1(t) \ldots u_M(t)] \tag{A.2}$$

is the t-th row of U, defined in (5.4.4).

The moment generating function of the distribution in (A.1) is

$$M(t_1, \ldots, t_M) = \exp\left(\tfrac{1}{2} \sum_i \sum_j t_i t_j \sigma_{ij}\right) \tag{A.3}$$

and, therefore, in general

$$E\{u_i(t) u_j(t) u_k(t) u_l(t)\} = \left[\frac{\partial^4 M(t_1, \ldots, t_M)}{\partial t_i \partial t_j \partial t_k \partial t_l}\right]_{t_1 = \ldots = t_M = 0}$$

$$= \sigma_{ij}\sigma_{kl} + \sigma_{ik}\sigma_{jl} + \sigma_{il}\sigma_{jk},$$

for all $i, j, k, l = 1, \ldots, M$.

APPENDIX B. EXPECTATIONS REQUIRED FOR PROVING THEOREM I STATED IN SECTION 6.2

B.1 First of all we shall prove that

$$E(U'M^*u_i u'_j F_j U) = n_j (\Lambda \sigma_i \sigma'_j + \sigma_j \sigma'_i + \sigma_{ij} \Sigma) \tag{B.1}$$

where $n_j = m_j + l_j$ is the number of coefficients to be estimated in the j-th equation of the complete system (5.2.1), and F_j has been defined in (6.3.23).

We observe that $E(U'M^*u_i u'_j F_j U)$ is an $M \times M$ matrix, the term in the μ-th row and μ'-th column being

$$\sum_t \sum_{t'} \sum_{t''} \sum_{t'''} m^*_{tt'} f_j(t'', t''') E\{u_\mu(t) u_i(t') u_j(t'') u_{\mu'}(t''')\} \tag{B.2}$$

where $m^*_{tt'}$ is the term in the t-th row and the t'-th column of $M^* = X(X'X)^{-1}X'$ and $f_j(t'', t''')$ is the term in the t''-th row and t'''-th column of the $T \times T$ matrix F_j defined in (6.3.23). The respective terms in the expectation involved in (B.2) are non-zero only in the following cases and then their respective contribution to (B.2) is as follows:

Cases	Contribution to (B.2)
$t = t' = t'' = t'''$	$\sum_t m^*_{tt} f_j(t, t) \, (\sigma_{\mu i} \sigma_{j\mu'} + \sigma_{\mu j}\, \sigma_{i\mu'} + \sigma_{\mu\mu'}\, \sigma_{ij})$
$t = t',\, t'' = t'''$ but $t \neq t''$	$\sigma_{i\mu}\, \sigma_{j\mu'} \, \{(\sum_t m^*_{tt})\, (\sum_{t''} f_j(t'', t'')) - \sum_t m^*_{tt} f_j(t, t)\}$
$t = t'',\, t' = t'''$ but $t \neq t'$	$\sigma_{\mu j}\, \sigma_{i\mu'} \, \{\sum_t \sum_{t'} m^*_{tt'} f_j(t, t') - \sum_t m^*_{tt} f_j(t, t)\}$
$t = t''',\, t' = t''$ but $t \neq t'$	$\sigma_{\mu\mu'}\, \sigma_{ij} \, \{\sum_t \sum_{t'} m^*_{tt'} f_j(t', t) - \sum_t m^*_{tt} f_j(t, t)\}.$

Adding these results we obtain

$$\sum_t \sum_{t'} \sum_{t''} \sum_{t'''} m^*_{tt'} f_j(t'', t''') E\{u_\mu(t) u_i(t') u_j(t'') u_{\mu'}(t''')\}$$

$$= \sigma_{\mu i} \sigma_{j\mu'} (\text{tr}M^*)(\text{tr}F_j) + \sigma_{\mu j} \sigma_{i\mu'},\, \text{tr}(M^* F_j) + \sigma_{\mu\mu'} \sigma_{ij}\, \text{tr}(M^* F_j'), \tag{B.3}$$

where

$$\sum_t m^*_{tt} = \text{tr}M^* = \text{tr}\{X(X'X)^{-1}X'\} = \text{tr}\{(X'X)^{-1}X'X\} = \Lambda,$$

$$\sum_t f_j(t, t) = \text{tr}F_j = \text{tr}\{XC_jQ_jC_j'X'\} = \text{tr}\{Q_jC_j'X'XC_j\} = n_j = m_j + l_j$$

and $\tag{B.4}$

$$\sum_t \sum_{t'} m^*_{tt'} f_j(t, t') = \text{tr}(M^* F_j) = \text{tr}F_j = n_j,$$

because F_j is symmetric. The result in (B.1) then follows immediately.

We can now directly obtain the following expectations from (B.1).

97

$$E(U'M^*u_iu_j'M^*U) = \Lambda(\Lambda\sigma_i\sigma_j' + \sigma_j\sigma_i' + \sigma_{ij}\,\Sigma), \tag{B.5}$$

$$E(U'F_iu_iu_j'F_jU) = \{n_in_j\sigma_i\sigma_j' + (\sigma_j\sigma_i' + \sigma_{ij}\Sigma)\,\mathrm{tr}(Q_iQ_{ij}Q_jQ_{ij}')\}. \tag{B.6}$$

The former expectation is obtained by replacing F_j by M^* in (B.1) and the latter by replacing M^* by F_i therein.

B.2 Next let us prove that

$$E(U'M^*u_iu_j'G_jU') = (\Lambda\sigma_i\sigma_j' + \sigma_j\sigma_i' + \sigma_{ij}\Sigma)\,G_j', \tag{B.7}$$

where G_j has been defined in (6.3.24).

In this case $E(U'M^*u_iu_j'G_jU')$ is an $M \times T$ matrix, the term in the μ-th row and t-th column of which is

$$\sum_{\mu'}\sum_{t'}\sum_{t''}\sum_{t'''} m^*_{t't''}\,g_j(t''', \mu')\,E\{u_\mu(t')u_i(t'')u_j(t''')u_{\mu'}(t)\}. \tag{B.8}$$

such that as before $m^*_{t't''}$ is the term in the t'-th row and t''-th column of M^* and $g_j(t''', \mu')$ is the term in the t'''-th row and μ'-th column of the $T \times M$ matrix, $G_j = XC_jQ_jD_j'$. Considering the individual terms in the summation in (B.8) we find that they are non-zero only in the following cases and their respective contribution is as noted below.

Cases	Contribution to (B.8)
$t' = t'' = t''' = t$	$\sum_{\mu'} m^*_{tt}g_j(t, \mu')\,\{\sigma_{ij}\,\sigma_{\mu\mu'} + \sigma_{i\mu}\,\sigma_{j\mu'} + \sigma_{i\mu'}\,\sigma_{j\mu}\}$
$t' = t'',\, t''' = t$ but $t' \neq t$	$\{\sum_{\mu'}\sum_{t'} m^*_{t't'}g_j(t, \mu') - \sum_{\mu'} m^*_{tt}g_j(t, \mu')\}\,\sigma_{i\mu}\,\sigma_{j\mu'}$
$t'' = t''',\, t' = t$ but $t'' \neq t$	$\{\sum_{\mu'}\sum_{t''} m^*_{tt''}\,g_j(t'', \mu') - \sum_{\mu'} m^*_{tt}g_j(t, \mu')\}\,\sigma_{ij}\,\sigma_{\mu\mu'}$
$t''' = t',\, t'' = t$ but $t' \neq t$	$\{\sum_{\mu'}\sum_{t'} m^*_{tt'}g_j(t', \mu') - \sum_{\mu'} m^*_{tt}g_j(t, \mu')\}\,\sigma_{\mu j}\,\sigma_{i\mu'}.$

Therefore, the sum in (B.8) is equal to

$$\Lambda\,\sigma_{i\mu}\sum_{\mu'}\sigma_{j\mu'}g_j(t, \mu') + \sigma_{ij}\sum_{\mu'}\sum_{t''}\sigma_{\mu\mu'}m^*_{tt''}g_j(t'', \mu') +$$
$$+ \sigma_{\mu j}\sum_{\mu'}\sum_{t'}\sigma_{i\mu'}m^*_{tt'}g_j(t', \mu'), \tag{B.9}$$

and noting that

$$G_j'M^* = G_j', \tag{B.10}$$

we arrive at the result stated in (B.7).

The following expectation can then be derived from (B.7) by replacing M^* by the $T \times T$ matrix $F_i = XC_iQ_iC_i'X'$;

$$E(U'F_iu_iu_j'G_jU') = n_i\sigma_i\sigma_j'G_j' + \sigma_j\sigma_i'G_j'F_i + \sigma_{ij} \Sigma G_j'F_i. \tag{B.11}$$

Now if we consider the transpose of (B.11) with i and j interchanged we get

$$E(UG_i'u_iu_j'F_jU) = n_jG_i\sigma_i\sigma_j' + F_jG_i\sigma_j\sigma_i' + \sigma_{ij} F_jG_i \Sigma, \tag{B.12}$$

because F_i is symmetric.

B.3 We now proceed to prove that

$$E(u_iu_j'G_jU'M^*U) = G_j (\sigma_i\sigma_j' + \sigma_j\sigma_i' + \Lambda\sigma_{ij} \Sigma). \tag{B.13}$$

The term in the t-th row and the μ-th column of the $T \times M$ matrix on the left hand side of (B.13) is

$$\sum_{\mu'} \sum_{t'} \sum_{t''} \sum_{t'''} g_j(t', \mu')m^*_{t'', t'''} E\{u_i(t)u_j(t')u_{\mu'}(t'')u_\mu(t''')\}, \tag{B.14}$$

and we may analyze the following cases:

Cases	Contribution to (B.14)
$t' = t'' = t''' = t$	$\sum_{\mu'} g_j(t, \mu')m^*_{tt} (\sigma_{ij} \sigma_{\mu\mu'} + \sigma_{i\mu} \sigma_{j\mu'} + \sigma_{i\mu'} \sigma_{j\mu})$
$t' = t'', t''' = t$ but $t' \neq t$	$\{\sum_{\mu'} \sum_{t'} g_j(t', \mu')m^*_{t't} - \sum_{\mu'} g_j(t, \mu')m^*_{tt}\} \sigma_{i\mu} \sigma_{j\mu'}$
$t' = t''', t'' = t$ but $t' \neq t$	$\{\sum_{\mu'} \sum_{t'} g_j(t', \mu')m^*_{tt'} - \sum_{\mu'} g_j(t, \mu')m^*_{tt}\} \sigma_{j\mu} \sigma_{i\mu'}$
$t'' = t''', t' = t$ but $t'' \neq t$	$\{\sum_{\mu'} \sum_{t''} g_j(t, \mu')m^*_{t''t'''} - \sum_{\mu'} g_j(t, \mu')m^*_{tt}\} \sigma_{ij} \sigma_{\mu\mu'}$

This provides us the value of the summation in (B.14);

99

$$\sigma_{i\mu} \sum_{\mu'} \sum_{t'} \sigma_{j\mu'} g_j(t', \mu') m^*_{t't} + \sigma_{j\mu} \sum_{\mu'} \sum_{t'} \sigma_{i\mu'} g_j(t', \mu') m^*_{tt'} +$$

$$+ \Lambda \sigma_{ij} \sum_{\mu'} \sigma_{\mu\mu'} g_j(t, \mu') \tag{B.15}$$

which leads to the result given in (B.13), remembering that $M^*G_j = G_j$.

The following expectation is then a direct consequence of the above result in (B.13):

$$E(u_i u_j' G_j U' F_j U) = G_j (\sigma_i \sigma_j' + \sigma_j \sigma_i' + n_j \sigma_{ij} \Sigma), \tag{B.16}$$

where $F_j G_j = G_j$.

B.4 Now consider the following expectation

$$E(u_i u_j' M^* U G_j' U) = G_j (\sigma_i \sigma_j' + \Lambda \sigma_j \sigma_i' + \sigma_{ij} \Sigma). \tag{B.17}$$

To prove this result we observe that the expectation on the left hand side of (B.17) is a $T \times M$ matrix, the term in the t-th row and the μ-th column being

$$\sum_{\mu'} \sum_{t'} \sum_{t''} \sum_{t'''} m^*_{t''t} g_j(t''', \mu') \, E\{u_i(t)u_j(t')u_{\mu'}(t'')u_\mu(t''')\}. \tag{B.18}$$

The successive terms in this summation are non-zero only in the following cases and their contribution to (B.18) in each case is as noted below:

Cases	*Contribution to* (B.18)
$t' = t'' = t''' = t$	$\sum_{\mu'} m^*_{tt} g_j(t, \mu') \{\sigma_{ij} \sigma_{\mu\mu'} + \sigma_{i\mu} \sigma_{j\mu'} + \sigma_{i\mu'} \sigma_{j\mu}\}$
$t' = t'', t''' = t$ but $t' \neq t$	$\{\sum_{\mu'} \sum_{t'} m^*_{t't} g_j(t, \mu') - \sum_{\mu'} m^*_{tt} g_j(t, \mu')\} \sigma_{\mu i} \sigma_{j\mu'}$
$t' = t''', t'' = t$ but $t' \neq t$	$\{\sum_{\mu'} \sum_{t'} m^*_{t't} g_j(t', \mu') - \sum_{\mu'} m^*_{tt} g_j(t, \mu')\} \sigma_{\mu' i} \sigma_{j\mu}$
$t'' = t''', t' = t$ but $t'' \neq t$	$\{\sum_{\mu'} \sum_{t''} m^*_{tt''} g_j(t'', \mu') - \sum_{\mu'} m^*_{tt} g_j(t, \mu')\} \sigma_{ij} \sigma_{\mu\mu'}$

Sum of these cases yields the value of the sum in (B.18):

$$\sigma_{ij} \sum_{\mu'} \sum_{t''} \sigma_{\mu\mu'} m^*_{tt''} g_j(t'', \mu') + \sigma_{j\mu} \sum_{\mu'} \sum_{t'} \sigma_{i\mu'} m^*_{tt'} g_j(t', \mu') +$$

$$+ \sigma_{i\mu} \left(\sum_{t'} m^*_{t't'} \right) \sum_{\mu'} \sigma_{j\mu'} g_j(t, \mu'), \tag{B.19}$$

and this provides the result in (B.17).

Using (B.17), it follows that

$$E(u_i u'_j F_j U G'_j U) = G_j \left(\sigma_i \sigma'_j + n_j \sigma_j \sigma'_i + \sigma_{ij} \Sigma \right), \tag{B.20}$$

because $F_j G_j = G_j$.

B.5 Next we prove that

$$E(u_i u'_j M^* U H_j U')$$
$$= \Lambda(\sigma'_i H_j \sigma_j) \cdot I + (\sigma'_i H_j \sigma_j) M^* + \sigma_{ij} \, \mathrm{tr}(H_j \, \Sigma) M^*. \tag{B.21}$$

This is a $T \times T$ matrix of which the term in the t-th row and the t'-th column is

$$\sum_{\mu} \sum_{\mu'} \sum_{t''} \sum_{t'''} m^*_{t''t'''} h_j \, (\mu, \mu') \, E\{u_i(t)u_j(t'')u_\mu(t''')u_{\mu'}(t')\}, \tag{B.22}$$

where $h_j(\mu, \mu')$ is the term in the μ-th row and μ'-th column of the $M \times M$ matrix $H_j = D_j Q_j D'_j$ defined in (6.3.28). The evaluation of successive terms in the summation (B.22) involves the following non-zero cases:

Cases	*Contribution to* (B.22)
On the diagonal $(t' = t)$: $t' = t'' = t''' = t$	$\sum_{\mu} \sum_{\mu'} m^*_{tt} h_j(\mu, \mu') \, (\sigma_{ij} \, \sigma_{\mu\mu'} + \sigma_{i\mu} \, \sigma_{j\mu'} + \sigma_{i\mu'} \, \sigma_{j\mu})$
$t'' = t''', t' = t$ but $t'' \neq t$	$\{\sum_{\mu} \sum_{\mu'} \sum_{t''} m^*_{t''t''} h_j(\mu, \mu') - \sum_{\mu} \sum_{\mu'} m^*_{tt} h_j(\mu, \mu')\} \, \sigma_{i\mu'} \, \sigma_{j\mu}$
Off-diagonal $(t' \neq t)$: $t''' = t', t'' = t$	$\sum_{\mu} \sum_{\mu'} m^*_{tt'} h_j(\mu, \mu') \, \sigma_{ij} \, \sigma_{\mu\mu'}$
$t'' = t', t''' = t$	$\sum_{\mu} \sum_{\mu'} m^*_{t't} h_j(\mu, \mu') \, \sigma_{i\mu} \, \sigma_{j\mu'}$

Therefore, on the diagonal, when $t' = t$, the summation (B.22) is equal to

$$\Lambda \sum_\mu \sum_{\mu'} h_j(\mu, \mu') \sigma_{i\mu'} \sigma_{j\mu} + \sum_\mu \sum_{\mu'} m_{tt}^* h_j(\mu, \mu') \times$$

$$(\sigma_{ij} \sigma_{\mu\mu'} + \sigma_{i\mu} \sigma_{j\mu'}), \tag{B.23}$$

and off-diagonal ($t \neq t'$) the value of (B.22) is

$$m_{tt'}^* \sigma_{ij} \sum_\mu \sum_{\mu'} h_j(\mu, \mu') \sigma_{\mu\mu'} + m_{t't}^* \sum_\mu \sum_{\mu'} h_j(\mu, \mu') \sigma_{i\mu} \sigma_{j\mu'}. \tag{B.24}$$

This leads to the result stated in (B.21). Furthermore, it follows that

$$E(u_i u_j' F_j U H_j U') = n_j(\sigma_i' H_j \sigma_j) \cdot I + (\sigma_i' H_j \sigma_j) F_j +$$

$$+ \sigma_{ij} \operatorname{tr}(H_j \Sigma) F_j, \tag{B.25}$$

where use has been made of (B.21) and (6.3.23).

B.6 Now let us prove that

$$E(u_i u_j' G_j U' G_j U') = (\sigma_i' H_j \sigma_j) \cdot I + G_j \sigma_j \sigma_i' G_j' + \sigma_{ij} G_j \Sigma G_j', \tag{B.26}$$

where it should be noted that $G_j' G_j = H_j$, G_j and H_j having been defined in (6.3.24) and (6.3.28), respectively.

The expectation on the left hand side of (B.26) is a $T \times T$ matrix, the term in the t-th row and t'-th column being

$$\sum_\mu \sum_{\mu'} \sum_{t''} \sum_{t'''} g_j(t'', \mu) g_j(t''', \mu') E\{u_i(t)u_j(t'')u_\mu(t''')u_{\mu'}(t')\}. \tag{B.27}$$

Considering the successive terms in (B.27) we arrive at the following cases:

Cases	Contribution to (B.27)
On the diagonal $(t' = t)$:	
$t' = t'' = t''' = t$	$\sum_\mu \sum_{\mu'} g_j(t, \mu) g_j(t, \mu') \{\sigma_{ij} \sigma_{\mu\mu'} + \sigma_{i\mu} \sigma_{j\mu'} + \sigma_{i\mu'} \sigma_{j\mu}\}$
$t'' = t'''$, $t' = t$ but $t'' \neq t$	$\{\sum_\mu \sum_{\mu'} \sum_{t''} g_j(t'', \mu) g_j(t'', \mu') - \sum_\mu \sum_{\mu'} g_j(t, \mu) g_j(t, \mu')\}$ $\sigma_{i\mu'} \sigma_{j\mu}$
Off-diagonal $(t' \neq t)$:	
$t''' = t'$, $t'' = t$	$\{\sum_\mu \sum_{\mu'} g_j(t, \mu) g_j(t', \mu')\} \sigma_{ij} \sigma_{\mu\mu'}$
$t'' = t'$, $t''' = t$	$\{\sum_\mu \sum_{\mu'} g_j(t', \mu) g_j(t, \mu')\} \sigma_{i\mu} \sigma_{j\mu'}.$

Hence, on the diagonal $(t' = t)$ the summation in (B.27) is

$$\{ \sum_{\mu} \sum_{\mu'} g_j(t, \mu) g_j(t, \mu') \} (\sigma_{ij} \sigma_{\mu\mu'} + \sigma_{i\mu} \sigma_{j\mu'}) +$$

$$+ \{ \sum_{\mu} \sum_{\mu'} \sum_{t''} g_j(t'', \mu) g_j(t'', \mu') \} \sigma_{i\mu'} \sigma_{j\mu}, \tag{B.28}$$

and off-diagonal $(t' \neq t)$ it is

$$\{ \sum_{\mu} \sum_{\mu'} g_j(t, \mu) g_j(t', \mu') \} \sigma_{ij} \sigma_{\mu\mu'} +$$

$$+ \{ \sum_{\mu} \sum_{\mu'} g_j(t', \mu) g_j(t, \mu') \} \sigma_{i\mu} \sigma_{j\mu'}. \tag{B.29}$$

Hence, we get the result stated in (B.26).

B.7 Lastly, we have the following result:

$$E(U G_i' u_i u_j' G_j U') = \sigma_{ij} \, \mathrm{tr}(G_i \, \Sigma \, G_j') \cdot I + G_i \sigma_i \sigma_j' G_j' + G_j \sigma_i \sigma_j' G_i'. \tag{B.30}$$

The expectation on the left hand side of (B.30) is a $T \times T$ matrix, the term in the t-th row and t'-th column being

$$\sum_{\mu} \sum_{\mu'} \sum_{t''} \sum_{t'''} g_i(t'', \mu) g_j (t''', \mu') \, E\{u_\mu(t) u_i(t'') u_j(t''') u_{\mu'}(t')\}, \tag{B.31}$$

the successive terms in (B.31) are non-zero only in the following cases:

Cases	*Contribution to* (B.31)
On the diagonal $(t' = t)$:	
$t' = t'' = t''' = t$	$\sum_{\mu} \sum_{\mu'} g_i(t, \mu) g_j(t, \mu') (\sigma_{ij} \sigma_{\mu\mu'} + \sigma_{i\mu} \sigma_{j\mu'} + \sigma_{i\mu'} \sigma_{\mu j})$
$t'' = t''', t' = t$ but $t'' \neq t$	$\{ \sum_{\mu} \sum_{\mu'} \sum_{t''} g_i(t'', \mu) g_j(t'', \mu') - \sum_{\mu} \sum_{\mu'} g_i(t, \mu) g_j(t, \mu') \}$ $\sigma_{ij} \sigma_{\mu\mu'}$
Off-diagonal $(t' \neq t)$:	
$t''' = t', t'' = t$	$\sum_{\mu} \sum_{\mu'} g_i(t, \mu) g_j(t', \mu') \sigma_{i\mu} \sigma_{j\mu'}$
$t'' = t', t''' = t$	$\sum_{\mu} \sum_{\mu'} g_i(t', \mu) g_j(t, \mu') \sigma_{j\mu} \sigma_{i\mu'}.$

Therefore, on the diagonal ($t' = t$) the value of the summation in (B.31) is

$$\{ \sum_{\mu} \sum_{\mu'} g_i(t, \mu)\, g_j(t, \mu')\} (\sigma_{i\mu}\, \sigma_{j\mu'} + \sigma_{i\mu'}\, \sigma_{j\mu}) +$$

$$+ \sum_{\mu} \sum_{\mu'} \sum_{t''} g_i(t'', \mu)\, g_j(t'', \mu')\, \sigma_{\mu\mu'}\, \sigma_{ij}, \tag{B.32}$$

and off-diagonal ($t' \neq t$) (B.31) is equal to

$$\sum_{\mu} \sum_{\mu'} g_i(t, \mu)\, g_j(t', \mu')\, \sigma_{i\mu}\sigma_{j\mu'} + \sum_{\mu} \sum_{\mu'} g_i(t', \mu)\, g_j(t, \mu')\, \sigma_{j\mu}\, \sigma_{i\mu'}. \tag{B.33}$$

This leads to the result stated in (B.30).

NOTES

1. Comparing our notation with that of Nagar (1961) we have $C_1 = W$, $C = \Omega_{ii}$ and $\sigma^2 = \sigma_{ii}$.
2. This is not true if x_t takes values 1, 2, ..., T.
3. Here a brief discussion on the validity of the expansion seems in order. Recently, Richardson (1968) derived the exact sampling distribution of the two-stage least squares estimator and proved that the estimator possesses exact moments up to order K-1 where K is the number of exogenous variables excluded from the structural equation to be estimated. In a more recent article Nagar and Amanullah (1970) showed that the results presented in (1959a) on the bias, to order $1/T$, and the second moment, to order $1/T^2$ in probability, of the two-stage least squares estimator can be directly obtained from the exact expressions of the bias and second moment given by Richardson by retaining leading terms in the asymptotic expansion of the confluent hypergeometric functions. It follows that the methodology adopted here for approximating moments up to a finite order in probability is justified at least when the exact moments exist. For other related works refer to Sawa (1969) and Takeuchi (1970).
4. Throughout the chapter it is assumed that summation over t with whatever accent is from 1 through T and that over μ, μ' extends from 1 through M.
5. Cf. Wilks (1943), p. 39.

7. A numerical example: application to Klein's model I

In this chapter we illustrate numerically the moment matrix, to order $1/T^2$, of the two-stage least squares coefficient estimates and the bias of the estimate of the contemporaneous covariance matrix of the structural disturbances derived in the preceding chapter. We shall use Klein's six-equation model for this purpose.[1]

The results presented in Table 7.3 show practically no difference between the asymptotic and corrected, to order $1/T^2$, covariances of the two-stage least squares estimates of coefficients of the consumption versus demand for labour and investment versus demand for labour equations. In case of third pair of equations, namely consumption and investment, the two types of covariance estimates differ both in sign and magnitude. From the results given in Table 7.2 it can be seen that all the variance estimates s_{ii} and two of the three covariance estimates s_{ij} are negatively biased. The bias of the covariance estimate of disturbances between consumption and investment equations is the largest and that between investment and demand for labour is the smallest of three estimates.

7.2 DESCRIPTION OF THE MODEL

Klein's six-equation model of the U.S. economy (for the period 1921-41) consists of three behaviour equations and three identities. The first of these relates linearly total consumption (C) to current and lagged profits (π and π_{-1}) and wages ($W_1 + W_2$), W_1 and W_2 being the private and government wage bills, respectively;

$$\text{Consumption:} \ C = \alpha_1 \pi + \alpha_2 \pi_{-1} + \alpha_3 (W_1 + W_2) + u_1, \tag{7.2.1}$$

with u_1 as the structural disturbance.

The second equation describes net investment (I) as a linear function

105

of profits, both current and lagged (π and π_{-1}), and capital stock at the beginning of a year (K_{-1});

$$\text{Investment: } I = \beta_1 \pi + \beta_2 \pi_{-1} + \beta_3 K_{-1} + u_2, \tag{7.2.2}$$

u_2 being the disturbance in the equation.

The third equation is the demand for labour equation. This relates linearly private wages paid (W_1) to private product, both current and lagged (E and E_{-1}), and time t. The private product includes national income (Y), business taxes (T) and excludes wages paid by the government (W_2). Thus,

$$\text{Private wages: } W_1 = \gamma_1 E + \gamma_2 E_{-1} + \gamma_3 (t\text{-}1931) + u_3, \tag{7.2.3}$$

where $E = Y + T - W_2$ and u_3 is the disturbance term.

The remaining three equations are identities;

$$\text{Product: } \qquad Y + T \overset{\text{def}}{=} C + I + G, \tag{7.2.4}$$

$$\text{Income: } \qquad Y \overset{\text{def}}{=} \pi + W_1 + W_2, \tag{7.2.5}$$

and

$$\text{Capital: } \qquad K \overset{\text{def}}{=} K_{-1} + I, \tag{7.2.6}$$

where G is the government expenditure and K the capital stock.

In this model we have six endogenous variables, viz., C, π, W_1, I, Y and K, which are 'to be explained' with the help of seven lagged endogenous and exogenous variables, π_{-1}, K_{-1}, $(Y + T - W_2)_{-1}$, t, T, G and W_2. We shall deal with all these variables measured from their respective means and, therefore, constant term in each of the equations of the above system has not been included. Further, we shall consider only the first five equations (7.2.1) to (7.2.5) in the structural equation system for our exercise and omit the last identity, viz., $K \overset{\text{def}}{=} K_{-1} + I$.

The time series observations on all the jointly dependent and predetermined variables for the period 1921-41 are given in Klein (1950) and are measured in billions of 1934 U.S. dollars except the time variable t which is measured by the years, i.e., 1921, 1922, . . .

7.3 COMPUTATIONAL PROCEDURE AND THE RESULTS

Since we are not considering the identity (7.2.6) as part of the complete system for obtaining numerical estimates of the structural parameters of Klein's model I, we are left with five equations given in (7.2.1) to (7.2.5) containing five jointly dependent variables, viz., C, π, W_1, I, and Y and seven lagged endogenous and exogenous variables, π_{-1}, K_{-1}, $(Y+T-W_2)_{-1}$, t, T, G and W_2 in the structural system. Thus, in this case $M = 3$, $\Lambda = 7$ and $T = 21$ and so the Assumption 3, stated in Section 5.5 is satisfied.

In the first instance, we estimate the asymptotic covariance matrix given in (6.2.16) of the two-stage least squares estimates of coefficients in different equations by using

$$\text{estimate of } Q_i = \hat{Q}_i = \begin{bmatrix} Y_i' Y_i - V_i' V_i & Y_i' X_i \\ \\ X_i' Y_i & X_i' X_i \end{bmatrix}^{-1} \quad \begin{matrix} (7.3.1) \\ [\text{cf. (6.2.2)}], \end{matrix}$$

$$\text{estimate of } Q_{ij} = \hat{Q}_{ij} = \begin{bmatrix} Y_i' Y_j - V_i' V_j & Y_i' X_j \\ \\ X_i' Y_j & X_i' X_j \end{bmatrix} \quad \begin{matrix} (7.3.2) \\ [\text{cf. (6.2.3)}], \end{matrix}$$

and

$$\text{estimate of } \sigma_{ij} = \hat{\sigma}_{ij} = \frac{1}{T}(y_i - Y_i c_i - X_i b_i)'(y_j - Y_j c_j - X_j b_j), \quad (7.3.3)$$

where c_i and b_i are the two-stage least squares estimates of the coefficients γ_i and β_i of the i-th equation (5.4.9), respectively, and the suffixes 'i' and 'j' indicate the pair of structural equations under consideration. σ_{ij} is, in fact, the element in the i-th row and j-th column of the covariance matrix Σ of the contemporaneous structural disturbances defined in (5.5.1).

Furthermore, the correction, to order $1/T^2$, to be applied to the asymptotic covariance matrix of the coefficients in different equations may be obtained by computing

$$\text{estimate of } \Omega_{ij} = \hat{\Omega}_{ij} = \begin{bmatrix} \frac{1}{T} V_i' V_j & 0 \\ \\ 0 & 0 \end{bmatrix} \quad \begin{matrix} (7.3.4) \\ [\text{cf. (6.2.6)}], \end{matrix}$$

and

$$\text{estimate of } q_{ij} = \hat{q}_{ij} = \begin{bmatrix} \frac{1}{T} V_i' \hat{u}_j \\ \\ 0 \end{bmatrix} \quad \begin{matrix} (7.3.5) \\ [\text{cf. (6.2.8)}], \end{matrix}$$

where

107

$$\hat{u}_j = y_j - Y_j c_j - X_j b_j \qquad (7.3.6) \text{ [cf. (5.4.9)].}$$

Thus, if we are calculating the moment matrix of the coefficient estimates of the consumption equation (7.2.1) and those of investment equation (7.2.2), we have $i = 1$ and $j = 2$ in the relationships (7.3.1) to (7.3.6) and

$$Y_1 = [\pi \ (W_1 + W_2)], \quad X_1 = \pi_{-1},$$

$$Y_2 = \pi, \qquad\qquad X_2 = [\pi_{-1} \ K_{-1}],$$

$$V_1 = Y_1 - X(X'X)^{-1} X'Y_1,$$

$$V_2 = Y_2 - X(X'X)^{-1} X'Y_2, \qquad (7.3.7)$$

$$X = [\pi_{-1} \ K_{-1} \ E_{-1} \ (t\text{-}1931) \ T \ G \ W_2],$$

$$\hat{u}_1 = C - \hat{\alpha}_1 \pi - \hat{\alpha}_2 \pi_{-1} - \hat{\alpha}_3 (W_1 + W_2),$$

$$\hat{u}_2 = I - \hat{\beta}_1 \pi - \hat{\beta}_2 \pi_{-1} - \hat{\beta}_3 K_{-1},$$

where each endogenous or exogenous variable in (7.3.7) represents the column vector of observations measured from its mean. For example, π denotes the column vector of deviations from the mean of observations on current profits and so on. Similarly, Y_1 is a $T \times 2$ matrix of deviations on current profits and wages, X_1 is a column vector of deviations on lagged profits etc., and $\hat{\alpha}_1, \hat{\alpha}_2, \hat{\alpha}_3, \hat{\beta}_1, \hat{\beta}_2, \hat{\beta}_3$ are the two-stage least squares estimates of $\alpha_1, \alpha_2, \alpha_3, \beta_1, \beta_2, \beta_3$, respectively.

From (7.3.1) to (7.3.7) it follows that in case of consumption and investment equations,

$$\hat{Q}_1 = \begin{bmatrix} 0.0133 & -0.0015 & -0.0092 \\ -0.0015 & 0.0016 & -0.0005 \\ -0.0092 & -0.0005 & 0.0110 \end{bmatrix},$$

$$\hat{Q}_2 = \begin{bmatrix} 0.0217 & -0.0186 & 0.0030 \\ -0.0186 & 0.0192 & -0.0028 \\ 0.0030 & -0.0028 & 0.0009 \end{bmatrix},$$

$$\hat{Q}_{12} = \begin{bmatrix} 294.2463 & 261.4933 & -168.8807 \\ 362.8476 & 352.6455 & 502.3323 \\ 261.4939 & 324.5181 & 123.2276 \end{bmatrix},$$

and, hence, we get an estimate of the asymptotic covariance matrix

$$\operatorname*{plim}_{T\to\infty} T\,E \begin{bmatrix} (\hat\alpha_1-\alpha_1)(\hat\beta_1-\beta_1) & (\hat\alpha_1-\alpha_1)(\hat\beta_2-\beta_2) & (\hat\alpha_1-\alpha_1)(\hat\beta_3-\beta_3) \\ (\hat\alpha_2-\alpha_2)(\hat\beta_1-\beta_1) & (\hat\alpha_2-\alpha_2)(\hat\beta_2-\beta_2) & (\hat\alpha_2-\alpha_2)(\hat\beta_3-\beta_3) \\ (\hat\alpha_3-\alpha_3)(\hat\beta_1-\beta_1) & (\hat\alpha_3-\alpha_3)(\hat\beta_2-\beta_2) & (\hat\alpha_3-\alpha_3)(\hat\beta_3-\beta_3) \end{bmatrix}$$

by using the relationship (6.2.16).

Further, for the finite sample moment matrix of the two-stage least squares estimates given in (6.2.10), we calculate

$$\hat\Omega_{11} = \begin{bmatrix} 2.9501 & 1.9799 & 0.0000 \\ 1.9799 & 1.9053 & 0.0000 \\ 0.0000 & 0.0000 & 0.0000 \end{bmatrix},$$

$$\hat\Omega_{12} = \begin{bmatrix} 2.9501 & 0.0000 & 0.0000 \\ 1.9799 & 0.0000 & 0.0000 \\ 0.0000 & 0.0000 & 0.0000 \end{bmatrix},$$

$$\hat\Omega_{22} = \begin{bmatrix} 2.9501 & 0.0000 & 0.0000 \\ 0.0000 & 0.0000 & 0.0000 \\ 0.0000 & 0.0000 & 0.0000 \end{bmatrix},$$

$$\hat q_{11} = \begin{bmatrix} 1.1368 \\ 0.5014 \\ 0.0000 \end{bmatrix}, \qquad \hat q_{12} = \begin{bmatrix} 1.6948 \\ 1.5084 \\ 0.0000 \end{bmatrix},$$

$$\hat q_{21} = \begin{bmatrix} 1.1368 \\ 0.0000 \\ 0.0000 \end{bmatrix}, \quad \text{and } \hat q_{22} = \begin{bmatrix} 1.6948 \\ 0.0000 \\ 0.0000 \end{bmatrix},$$

which provide an estimate of the finite sample moment matrix of the coefficients of consumption and investment equations in the model. The bias, to order $1/T$, of the two-stage least squares estimated contemporaneous covariance of the structural disturbances of consumption and investment equations is computed according to the expression given in (6.2.24).

In a similar fashion we obtain an estimate of the covariance matrix of the coefficients and the bias of the covariance estimates of structural disturbances of consumption and demand for labour equations and investment and demand for labour equations in Klein's model I.

The results of our computations are tabulated below.

Table 7.1   Two-stage least squares estimates of parameters in Klein's model I

| Equation | Two-Stage Least Squares Estimates | | |
	1	*2*	*3*
Consumption	0.0173	0.2162	0.8102
Investment	0.1502	0.6159	—0.1578
Demand for Labour	0.4389	0.1467	0.1304

The numbers 1, 2 and 3 in the top row of the table indicate the suffices of coefficients in an equation.

Table 7.2   Two-stage least squares estimated contemporaneous covariance matrix of structural disturbances and its bias*

Estimate (S) of the Covariance Matrix (Σ)			Bias to (0) T^{-1} of S		
1.0441			—0.2565		
0.4379	1.3832		—0.2728	—0.5488	
—0.3852	0.1926	0.4764	0.0806	—0.0203	—0.0796

* The estimate S of the covariance matrix Σ as given above is different from the estimator $((s_{\mu\mu'}))$ obtained by Zellner and Theil (1962, p. 75) because the latter is based on the assertion $X_R'\hat{U} = 0$ which is incorrect.

NOTE

1. Cf. Klein (1950), p. 58. It should be pointed out that some of the assumptions underlying our results given in the preceding chapter are violated in case of Klein's model I. The numerical results of our example are therefore of limited practical value. Since our aim here is simply to illustrate the computational procedure, we neglect this fact.

Table 7.3 *The covariances of coefficient estimates in Klein's six equation model*

Equation	Two-Stage Least-Squares Estimates	Investment			Demand for Labour		
		β_1: 0.1502	β_2: 0.6159	β_3: −0.1578	γ_1: 0.4389	γ_2: 0.1476	γ_3: 0.1304
(1)	(2)	(3)	(4)	(5)	(6)	(7)	(8)
Consumption	α_1: 0.0173	0.0040 (0.0070)	−0.0031 (−0.0059)	−0.0004 (0.0006)	−0.0018 (−0.0017)	0.0019 (0.0017)	0.0007 (0.0006)
	α_2: 0.2162	−0.0046 (−0.0055)	0.0051 (0.0055)	−0.0001 (−0.0006)	0.0012 (0.0011)	−0.0018 (−0.0017)	0.0005 (0.0005)
	α_3: 0.8102	0.0013 (−0.0001)	−0.0012 (0.0001)	0.0004 (0.0001)	0.0001 (0.0001)	−0.0001 (−0.0001)	−0.0005 (−0.0005)
Investment	β_1: 0.1502				0.0006 (0.0006)	−0.0006 (−0.0006)	0.0005 (0.0005)
	β_2: 0.6159				−0.0003 (−0.0003)	0.0006 (0.0007)	−0.0007 (−0.0007)
	β_3: −0.1578				−0.0001 (−0.0001)	0.0001 (0.0001)	0.0002 (0.0002)

Source of data: Klein's *Economic Fluctuations in the United States, 1921-41*, p. 135. Figures noted without brackets are the asymptotic covariances between the two-stage least squares estimates of coefficients in equations indicated. Those within brackets are obtained by applying finite sample corrections, to order $1/T^2$, according to formula (6.2.10).

References

ALT, F. L. (1942), 'Distributed Lags,' *Econometrica*, Vol. 10.

AMEMIYA, T. and W. A. FULLER (1967), 'A Comparative Study of Alternative Estimators in a Distributed Lag Model,' *Econometrica*, Vol. 35, pp. 509–29.

ANDERSON, T. W. and H. RUBIN (1949), 'Estimation of the Parameters of a Single Equation in a Complete System of Stochastic Equations,' *Annals of Mathematical Statistics*, Vol. 20, pp. 46–63.

ARROW, K. J., H. B. CHENERY, B. S. MINHAS and R. M. SOLOW (1961), 'Capital-Labour Substitution and Economic Efficiency,' *The Review of Economics and Statistics*, Vol. 43, p. 225.

BASMANN, R. L. (1957), 'A Generalized Classical Method of Linear Estimation of Coefficients in a Structural Equation,' *Econometrica*, Vol. 25, pp. 77–83.

— — — (1961), 'A Note on the Exact Finite Sample Frequency Functions of Generalized Classical Linear Estimators in Two Leading Over-identified Cases,' *Journal of the American Statistical Association*, Vol. 56, pp. 619–36.

BROWN, T. M. (1952), 'Habit Persistence and Lags in Consumer Behaviour,' *Econometrica*, Vol. 20, pp. 355-71.

CAGAN, PHILLIP D. (1956), 'The Monetary Dynamics of Hyperinflation,' in *Studies in the Quantity Theory of Money*, M. Friedman, Editor, University of Chicago Press, Chicago.

CHRIST, C. F. (1966), *Econometric Models and Methods*, John Wiley and Sons, Inc., New York.

COCHRANE, D. and G. H. ORCUTT (1949), 'Application of Least Squares Regression to Relationships Containing Autocorrelated Error Terms,' *Journal of the American Statistical Association*, Vol. 44, pp. 32–61.

CRAMÉR, H. (1946), *Mathematical Methods of Statistics*, Princeton University Press, Princeton.

DHRYMES, P. J. (1969), 'Efficient Estimation of Distributed Lags with Autocorrelated Errors,' *International Economic Review*, Vol. 10, pp. 47–67.

DUESENBERRY, J. S., G. FROMM, L. R. KLEIN and E. KUH (edited, 1965), *The Brookings Quarterly Econometric Model of the United States*, North Holland Publishing Company, Amsterdam.

FISHER, I. (1937), 'Note on a Short-Cut Method for Calculating Distributed Lags,' *Bulletin de L'Institut International de Statistique*, Vol. 29, La Haye, pp. 323–27.

FRIEDMAN, MILTON (1957), *A Theory of the Consumption Function*, Princeton University Press, Princeton.

GOLDBERGER, A. S. (1964), *Econometric Theory*, John Wiley and Sons, Inc., New York.

GUPTA, Y. P. (1968), 'The Moment Matrix of the Liviatan's Consistent Estimator in a Distributed Lag Model,' *Sankhyā: The Indian Journal of Statistics*, Series B, Parts 1 and 2, pp. 89–96.

HANNAN, E. J. (1965), 'The Estimation of Relationships Involving Distributed Lags,' *Econometrica*, Vol. 33, pp. 206–24.

HARBERGER, A. C. (ed. 1960), *The Demand for Durable Goods*, University of Chicago Press, Chicago.

JOHNSTON, J. (1963), *Econometric Methods*, McGraw-Hill Book Company, Inc., New York.

JORGENSON, D. W. (1966), 'Rational Distributed Lag Functions,' *Econometrica*, Vol. 34, pp. 135–49.

KLEIN, L. R. (1950), *Economic Fluctuations in the United States*, 1921–1941, John Wiley and Sons, Inc., New York.

— — — (1958), 'The Estimation of Distributed Lags,' *Econometrica*, Vol. 26, pp. 553–65.

— — — and A. S. GOLDBERGER (1955), *An Econometric Model of the United States*, 1929–52, North Holland Publishing Company, Amsterdam.

KOOPMANS, T. C. (1953), 'Identification Problems in Economic Model Construction,' Chapter 2 in *Studies in Econometric Method*, W. C. Hood and T. C. Koopmans, Editors, Cowles Commission Monograph 14, New York.

— — — and W. C. HOOD (1953), 'The Estimation of Simultaneous Linear Economic Relationships,' Chapter 6 in *Studies in Econometric Method*, W. C. Hood and T. C. Koopmans, Editors, Cowles Commission Monograph 14, John Wiley and Sons, Inc., New York.

— — —, H. RUBIN and R. B. LEIPNIK (1950), 'Measuring the Equation Systems of Dynamic Economics,' Chapter 2 in *Statistical Inference in Dynamic Economic Models*, T. C. Koopmans, Editor, Cowles Commission Monograph 10, John Wiley and Sons, Inc., New York.

KOYCK, L. M. (1954), *Distributed Lags and Investment Analysis*, North Holland Publishing Company, Amsterdam.

LECAM, L. and LORRAINE SCHWARTZ (1960), 'A Necessary and Sufficient Condition for the Existence of Consistent Estimates,' *Annals of Mathematical Statistics*, pp. 140–50.

LIVIATAN, N. (1963), 'Consistent Estimation of Distributed Lags,' *International Economic Review*, Vol. 4, pp. 44–52.

MALINVAUD, E. (1961), 'The Estimation of Distributed Lags: A Comment,' *Econometrica*, Vol. 29, pp. 430–33.

— — — (1966), *Statistical Methods of Econometrics*, North Holland Publishing Company, Amsterdam (Translation by Mrs. A. Silvey).

MISRA, P. N. and Y. P. GUPTA (1971), 'Estimation of the Covariance Matrix of Structural Disturbances in a Complete Equation System,' *Statistica Neerlandica*, Vol. 25, pp. 45–55.

MORRISON, J. L. (1970), 'Small Sample Properties of Selected Distributed Lag Estimators,' *International Economic Review*, Vol. 11, pp. 13–23.

NAGAR, A. L. (1959a), 'The Bias and Moment Matrix of the General k-Class Estimators of the Parameters in Simultaneous Equations,' *Econometrica*, Vol. 27, pp. 575–95.

— — — (1959b), *Statistical Estimation of Simultaneous Economic Relationships*, Unpublished Dissertation, Rotterdam.

— — — (1961), 'The Residual Variance Estimation in Simultaneous Equations,' *Econometrica*, Vol. 29, pp. 238–43.

— — — and AMANULLAH (1970), 'On Nagar's Approximations to Moments of the Two-Stage Least Squares Estimator,' presented at the *Second World Congress of the*

113

Econometric Society, Cambridge, England, September 8–14.

——— and Y. P. GUPTA (1968), 'The Bias of Liviatan's Consistent Estimator in a Distributed Lag Model,' *Econometrica*, Vol. 36, pp. 337–42.

——— (1970), 'The Moment Matrix of the Two-Stage Least Squares Estimator of Coefficients in Different Equations of a Complete System of Simultaneous Equations,' *Econometrica*, Vol. 38, pp. 39–49.

NERLOVE, M. (1958), *Distributed Lags and Demand Analysis for Agricultural and Other Commodities*, U.S. Department of Agriculture, Washington.

PALDA, KRISTIAN S. (1964), *The Measurement of Cumulative Advertising Effects*, Ford Foundation Doctoral Dissertation Series, Prentice-Hall.

RICHARDSON, DAVID H. (1968), 'The Exact Distribution of a Structural Coefficient Estimator,' *Journal of the American Statistical Association*, Vol. 63, pp. 1214–26.

SARGAN, J. D. (1958), 'The Estimation of Economic Relationships Using Instrumental Variables,' *Econometrica*, Vol. 26, pp. 393–415.

SAWA, T. (1969), 'The Exact Sampling Distribution of Ordinary Least Squares and Two-Stage Least Squares Estimators,' *Journal of the American Statistical Association*, Vol. 64, pp. 923–37.

SEWELL, WADE P. (1969), 'Least Squares, Conditional Predictions, and Estimator Properties,' *Econometrica*, Vol. 37, pp. 39–43.

SOLOW, R. M. (1960), 'On a Family of Lag Distributions,' *Econometrica*, Vol. 28, pp. 393–406.

TAKEUCHI, K. (1970), 'Exact Sampling Moments of the Ordinary Least Squares, Instrumental Variable, and Two-Stage Least Squares Estimators,' *International Economic Review*, Vol. 11, pp. 1–12.

THEIL, H. (1961), *Economic Forecasts and Policy*, North Holland Publishing Company, Amsterdam.

TINBERGEN, J. (1937), *An Econometric Approach to Business Cycle Problems*, Paris.

——— (1939), Statistical Testing of Business Cycle Theories, Vol. 2: *Business Cycles in the United States*, 1919–1932, Geneva.

——— (1949), 'Long-Term Foreign Trade Elasticities,' *Metroeconomica*, Vol. 1, p. 174.

——— (1951), *Business Cycles in the United Kingdom*, 1870–1914, Amsterdam.

TINTNER, G. (1954), *Econometrics*, John Wiley and Sons, Inc., New York.

WILKS, S. S. (1943), *Mathematical Statistics*, Princeton University Press, Princeton.

ZELLNER, A. and H. THEIL (1962), 'Three-Stage Least Squares: Simultaneous Estimation of Simultaneous Equations,' *Econometrica*, Vol. 30, pp. 54–78.

Index

Adjustment process, 12
Adoptive expectation model, 15
Alt, F. L., 10, 13, 33
Amanullah, 97
Amemiya, T., 6-7, 18, 24, 28-29, 35-36, 55
Anderson, T. W., 75
Arrow, K. J., 4
Asymptotically biased and unbiased estimators, *see* estimator

Basmann, R. L., 73, 75
Biased estimator, *see* estimator
Brookings econometric model, 4
Brown, T. M., 13

Cagan, P. D., 15
CES production function, 4
Chenery, H. B., 4
Christ, C. F., 34, 60
Cobb-Douglas production function, 4
Cochrane, D., 17
Cramér, H., 19, 44
Criteria for selecting instruments, 26

Dhrymes, P. J., 6-7, 18, 29, 31, 36
Discriminant function, 34
Distributed lags, 6, 8, 10-12, 29
existence of, 12
Distributed lag model (general), 5, 8, 12
estimation in (problems), 5, 13
alternative specifications, 13-15
with a geometric lag structure, 15-16, 28-29, 59-60
methods of estimation, 18
Disturbance term (concept), 6
Duesenberry, J. S., 4

Economic reaction, definition of, 11

Economic relationships (concept), 4-5
Error in variables model, 22
Estimation, in distributed lag models with geometric structure, 18-59
Amemiya, T. and W. A. Fuller's method, 28-29
Dhrymes' search, 29-33
Hannan's approach, 28
iterative instrumental variables procedure, 55-59
Klein's method, 22-25
Koyck's method, 20-22
(modified) Koyck's method, 34
least squares, 18-20
Liviatan's instrumental variables procedure, 25-28
numerical illustration, 59-66
in simultaneous equations, two-stage least squares, 73

Estimator (definition of)
asymptotically biased, 34
asymptotically unbiased, 34
biased, 33
consistent, 34
unbiased, 33

First order Markov scheme, 6, 17, 38, 60
Fisher, I., 10, 13, 33
Friedman, M., 15
Fromm, G., 4
Full-information maximum likelihood method, 75
Fuller, W. A., *see* Amemiya, T.

Gauss-Newton, 29
Generalised classical linear estimator in simultaneous equation models, 73, 75

115

Generalised least squares estimator in single equation models, 28, 56
Geometric curve, 15, 33
Geometric lag structure, definition of, 15
Goldberger, A. S., 4, 7
Gupta, Y. P., 9

Hannan, E. J., 6-7, 18, 27-28, 36, 55, 58-59
Harberger, A. C., 15
Homoscedasticity, 23
Hood, W. C., 6, 34

Identifiability criteria, 68-69
  order condition, 69
  rank condition, 69
Identified relation
  just-, 69
  not-, 70
  over-, 69

Johnston, J., 35
Jorgenson, D. W., 33

Klein, L. R., 4, 6-7, 18, 22-25, 36, 60, 62, 98-100, 102-103
  model I, 98-100, 103
Koopmans, T. C., 6, 34, 74-75
Koyck, L. M., 5-7, 10, 15-16, 18, 20-25, 33-34, 36, 60, 62
Kuh, E., 4

Lag distribution, 13, 33
Lag parameter, 15
LeCam, L., 34
Leipnik, R. B., 74-75
Limited-information maximum likelihood method, 75, 78
Linear curve, 14
Linearity of economic relationships, 4, 33
Liviatan, N., 6-8, 18, 22, 25, 27-28, 36-37, 40-41, 55, 58, 60-66
Log-normal curve, 14
Long-run marginal propensity to consume, 12, 62

Malinvaud, E., 7, 9, 16-17
Minhas, B. S., 4
Misra, P. N., 9
Modified Koyck procedure, *see* estimator
Moment generating function, 89

Moments of M-dimensional normal distribution, 89
Monte Carlo experiments, 27, **60**
Morrison, J. L., 27, 59
Multicollinearity, 13

Nagar, A. L., 9, 75-76, 97
Nerlove, M., 15, 33

Orcutt, G. H., *see* Cochrane, D.
Order in probability, 45-46

Palda, K. S., 15
Partial adjustment model, 15
Partial correlation, 27
Pascal family of lag distributions, 33
Probability limit of, 34
Proper instrument, 27, 35
Properties of the Liviatan's estimator, 36-54
  asymptotic covariance matrix, 42
  bias, 41
  moment matrix, 42
  residual variance estimator, 43
Properties of the two-stage least squares estimator, 75-97
  asymptotic covariance matrix, 79
  moment matrix, 78
  residual variance estimator, 80-81
  numerical illustration, 98-104

Reaction coefficient, definition of, 11
Reduced form, in distributed lag models, 22
  in simultaneous equation models, 70
  coefficients, 71
  disturbances, 71, 77
Residual, covariance estimator, 80
  variance estimator, 40, 43, 51, 81
Restrictions, zero type, 69, 74
Richardson, D. H., 97
Rubin, H., 74-75

Sargan, J. D., 56
Sawa, T., 97
Schwartz, L., *see* LeCam, L.
Sewell, W. P., 34
Short-run marginal propensity to consume, 12, 62
Simultaneous equations, general structural equation system, 67

116

complete, 68
Solow, R. M., 4, 33
Speed of adjustment, 12
Stability condition, 15, 33
Stochastic dependence, 6
Structural, coefficients, 67
   disturbances, 67

Takeuchi, K., 97
Theil, H., 8, 73, 75, 103
Three-stage least squares, 75
Time-shape of the economic reaction, 13-15
Tinbergen, J., 4, 10
Tintner's two-equation model, 68

Truncation remainder, 30
Two-stage least squares estimation procedure, 73

Variables
endogenous, 7, 67-68
   exogenous, 7, 67-68
   instrumental, 7, 25
   jointly dependent, 67-68
   predetermined, 7, 67-68

Wilks, S. S., 97

Zellner, A., 75, 103